NATIONAL GEOGRAPHIC LEARNING | CENGAGE Learning

D0491459

Life

UPPER INTERMEDIATE

Paul Dummett

NATIONAL GEOGRAPHIC LEARNING | CENGAGE Learning®

Life Upper Intermediate Workbook

Paul Dummett

Publisher: Jason Mann

Commissioning Editor: Alistair Baxter

Editorial Project Manager: Karen Spiller

Development Editor: Jess Rackham

Contributing Writer: Nick Kenny (IELTs practice test)

Marketing Manager: Michelle Cresswell

Project Editor: Amy Smith

Production Controller: Tom Relf

National Geographic Liaison: Leila Hishmeh

Cover design: Vasiliki Christoforidou

Text design: Vasiliki Christoforidou

Compositor: Q2AMedia Ltd

Audio: Prolingua Productions

© 2013 National Geographic Learning

ALL RIGHTS RESERVED. No part of this work covered by the copyright herein may be reproduced, transmitted, stored or used in any form or by any means graphic, electronic, or mechanical, including but not limited to photocopying, recording, scanning, digitising, taping, Web distribution, information networks, or information storage and retrieval systems, except as permitted under Section 107 or 108 of the 1976 United States Copyright Act, or applicable copyright law of another jurisdiction, without the prior written permission of the publisher.

For permission to use material from this text or product, submit all requests online at **cengage.com/permissions**

Further permissions questions can be emailed to **permissionrequest@cengage.com**

ISBN: 978-1-133-31546-9

National Geographic Learning
Cheriton House, North Way, Andover, Hampshire SP10 5BE
United Kingdom

Cengage Learning is a leading provider of customised learning solutions with office locations around the globe, including Singapore, the United Kingdom, Australia, Mexico, Brazil and Japan. Locate our local office at **international.cengage.com/region**

Cengage Learning products are represented in Canada by Nelson Education Ltd.

Visit National Geographic Learning at **http://elt.heinle.com**
Visit our corporate website at **www.cengage.com**

CREDITS

Although every effort has been made to contact copyright holders prior to publication, this has not always been possible. If notified, the publisher will undertake to rectify any errors or omissions at the earliest opportunity.

The publisher would like to thank the following sources for permission to reproduce their copyright protected text:

National Geographic for extracts adapted from 'Interview: "March of the Penguins" Director Luc Jacquet' by Stefan Lovgren, 24 June 2005, http://news.nationalgeographic.com, and 'Hayat Sindi, Science Entrepreneur', http://www.nationalgeographic.com, copyright © National Geographic. Reproduced with permission; VSO for an extract from 'Why Volunteer?', http://www.vso.org.uk/volunteer/why-volunteer/, Reproduced by permission of VSO; and The New York Public Library for an extract from 'The slave economy: How Slavery Helped Build a World Economy' by Howard Dodson, 2003, copyright © The New York Public Library. SciDev.Net for material adapted from 'How do I apply for a research grant?' by Thomas Egwang, Medical Biotechnology Labs, 13 February 2008, http://www.scidev.net. Used under the under a Creative Commons Attribution 2.0 licence; Tribune Media Services for an extract from 'Bright lights, bug city' by Philip Ball, *New Scientist* 22 February 2010, pp.35–37, copyright © 2010 Reed Business Information – UK. All rights reserved. Distributed by Tribune Media Services; Jodrell Bank Discovery Centre, for details about the centre, www.jodrellbank.net. Reproduced with permission; and Royal College of Physicians (RCP) for material adapted from *RCP Insight, Taking a split medical elective* by Peter Ellis, http://www.rcplondon.ac.uk, copyright © 2011 Royal College of Physicians. Adapted by permission.

The publisher would like to thank the following sources for permission to reproduce their copyright protected photos:

Cover: Paul Cheung/My Shot/National Geographic Image Collection

Inside: pp 4 (Jana Asenbrennerova/National Geographic My Shot), 6 (Shutterstock), 7 (laflor/iStockphoto), 8 (Stephen Bures/Alamy), 9 (Robert Fried/Alamy), 11 (Shutterstock), 12 (Frans Lanting/National Geographic Image Collection), 14 (Lee Cohen), 16 (Laura Stuzman/Sleeping Bear Press, a part of Cengage Learning), 18 (Fitzer/iStockphoto), 19 br (Dario Mitidieri/Getty Images), 19 tr (Joel Sartore/National Geographic Image Collection), 19 l (New Line/Saul Zaentz/Wing Nut/Kobal Images), 20 (dan_prat/iStockphoto), 22 (Catherine Karnow/National Geographic Image Collection), 23 (Stefano Cavoretto/Alamy), 24 (Renee Comet/National Geographic Image Collection), 28 (Shutterstock), 30 1 (Shutterstock), 30 2 (HeikeKampe/iStockphoto), 30 3 (LM Otero/AP/Press Association Images), 30 4 (Shutterstock), 30 5 (Shutterstock), 30 6 (Shutterstock), 30 7 (egal/iStockphoto), 30 bl (Shutterstock), 30 bc (Shutterstock), 32 (Jodi Cobb/National Geographic Image Collection), 33 (Shutterstock), 36 (James Nielsen/Getty Images), 38 (Terry Donnelly/Alamy), 39 (AKauroraPhotos/iStockphoto), 40 (chinaface/iStockphoto), 42 (fotoVoyager/iStockphoto), 44 (Eye Candy/Alamy), 45 (PanosKarapanagiotis/iStockphoto), 46 (MShep2/iStockphoto), 48 (Gordon Wiltsie/National Geographic Image Collection), 49 (Shutterstock), 52 (Greatstock Photographic Library/Alamy), 54 1 (landbysea/iStockphoto), 54 2 (leezsnow/iStockphoto), 54 3 (Shutterstock), 54 4 (MichaelUtech/iStockphoto), 54 5 (alantobey/iStockphoto), 54 6 (Shutterstock), 54 7 (Spinkle/iStockphoto), 54 8 (nesjerry/iStockphoto), 55 (dan_prat/iStockphoto), 56 tl (woraput/iStockphoto), 56 tc (lilly3/iStockphoto), 56 tr (vesilvio/iStockphoto), 57 (Andrew Woodley/Alamy), 60 (Gordon Gahan/National Geographic Image Collection), 62 (Joyce Dale/National Geographic Image Collection), 64 (Paul Nicklen/National Geographic Image Collection), 65 (pierredesvarre/iStockphoto), 66 (Thierry Planche/Fotolia), 68 (Alliance Images/Alamy), 70 (courtesy of Hayat Sindi), 72 (KeystoneUSA-ZUMA/Rex Pictures), 74 (LeggNet/iStockphoto), 75 l (Robert Harding Travel/Photolibrary), 75 r (Wes C. Skiles/National Geographic Image Collection), 76 (rossario/iStockphoto), 79 (Steve Raymer/National Geographic Image Collection), 81 (Kerstin Geier/Gallo Images/Corbis), 84 (Chris Rainier), 86 (FirePhoto/Alamy), 88 1 (Shutterstock), 88 2 (Shutterstock), 88 3 (Shutterstock), 88 4 (Shutterstock), 88 5 (Shutterstock), 88 br (Shutterstock), 92 (PeskyMonkey/iStockphoto), 94 (New York Historical Society), 96 (Maurice Joseph/Alamy), 97 (Shutterstock), 99 (Justin Guariglia/National Geographic Image Collection)

Illustrations by: Kevin Hopgood pp 25, 80

Printed in China by RR Donnelley
1 2 3 4 5 6 7 8 9 10 – 16 15 14 13 12

Contents

Unit 1	Relationships	page 4
Unit 2	Storytelling	page 12
Unit 3	Science and technology	page 20
Unit 4	Art and creativity	page 28
Unit 5	Development	page 36
Unit 6	Alternative travel	page 44
Unit 7	Natural resources	page 52
Unit 8	The news	page 60
Unit 9	Talented people	page 68
Unit 10	Customs and behaviour	page 76
Unit 11	Knowledge and learning	page 84
Unit 12	The economy	page 92
IELTs practice test		page 100
Audioscripts		page 114
Answer key		page 133

Unit 1 Relationships

1a A tradition in decline?

Reading friendships

1 Look at the photo. Then read the article. Which of the following statements best summarises the difference in the French and American attitudes to friendships?

a Most Americans have a lot of close friends.
b Americans are friendly with everyone; the French only with a few people.
c The French view friendship as something superficial.

2 Read the article again. Choose the correct option (a–c).

1 Which of the following relationships does the author NOT mention?
a colleagues
b fellow travellers
c fellow shoppers

2 Psychologists believe that in modern society … have become weaker.
a family relationships
b friendships
c all relationships

3 According to the article, 25% of Americans don't have … .
a strong family bonds
b a strong friendship
c any friends at all

4 Americans are known for being … people.
a lonely
b family-oriented
c friendly

5 French people are … about making friends.
a careful b worried c relaxed

6 The author thinks that in the West, we ignore the … of friendship.
a significance b qualities c security

3 Find nouns in the article derived from these adjectives.

1 true .....
2 strong .....
3 warm .....
4 long .....
5 deep .....

A tradition in decline?

Is intimate friendship a relationship that is dying out in modern society? In our busy lives, we have many acquaintances and friends – the people we work with, our neighbours, the people we chat to at the local shop and so on. But how many really close friendships can we count? The truth for most of us is probably not many. Some psychologists say that while we still value strong family bonds, in recent times, friendships have lost the strength and importance that they had in the past.

According to a study published recently in the USA, friendships in America have been declining in quality and quantity since at least 1985. The study claims that 25% of Americans don't have anyone they could call a close friend. Yet, on the surface, Americans seem extremely friendly people. If you have ever visited the USA, you will be familiar with the warmth and hospitality that they show to complete strangers. Everyone can be treated as a 'buddy', even if they are just a casual acquaintance.

But in other cultures, acquaintances and friendships have different qualities. In France, for example, when you are trying to get to know a person, they may seem rather unfriendly and the length of time it takes to form a strong friendship seems greater than in other countries. This is because for the French there is still a clear distinction between a casual acquaintance and a true friend. Although France is changing and perhaps becoming more like America, there is no doubt that French people are still more private in their friendships and that they reserve real intimacy for their closest friends. This intimacy can be found in many other non-western cultures too, where great importance is attached to the quality and depth of friendships. It is something that many of us in the West have forgotten and need to rediscover.

Glossary
die out (v) /ˌdaɪ ˈaʊt/ disappear
buddy (n) /ˈbʌdi/ a friend (colloquial)
intimacy (n) /ˈɪntɪməsi/ closeness in a relationship

Grammar present tenses review

4 Look at the article. Find examples of the following.

1 two progressive changes (present continuous)

.....

.....

2 two everyday activities (present simple)

.....

.....

3 two recent events with an impact on the present (present perfect simple)

.....

.....

4 one event that started in the past and continues now (present perfect continuous)

.....

5 Complete the questions from a survey on friendship. Use present tenses.

1 What person or people ..... (you / spend) most time with recently?

2 ..... (you / consider) this person or people to be close friends?

3 How many really close friends ..... (you / have)?

4 Would you say your friendship circle ..... (increase) or not?

5 ..... (you/make) any new friends in the past month?

6 How long ..... (you / know) your closest friend?

7 How often ..... (you / see) this person?

8 Generally, what qualities ..... (you / look for) in a friend?

Vocabulary friends: nouns and phrasal verbs

6 Look at the article again. Find the adjectives that collocate with these words. You may use the adjectives more than once.

1 a(n) ....., ..., ... friendship

2 a ..... bond

3 a ....., ... friend

4 a ..... stranger

5 a ..... acquaintance

7 Which word in each group does NOT collocate with the single word next to it? Cross out the word.

1 a mutual *friend / respect / student / interest*

2 a fellow *student / companion / scientist / traveller*

3 a close *acquaintance / relationship / friend / relative*

4 a *flat / faithful / travel* companion

5 a(n) *odd / happy / blood* couple

6 a(n) *fair-weather / old / passing* friend

8 Complete the sentences. Use the best collocation from Exercises 6 and 7.

1 Travelling alone can have its advantages, but I always prefer to have a ..... .

2 They are a very ..... : Kate is a highly-educated scientific researcher and Dan is a professional footballer who left school when he was fifteen.

3 Relationships where one person thinks they are better than the other don't work, but in this case they have a great ..... for each other.

4 Malcolm is probably my best friend. We were ..... at university.

5 I don't really consider Ann to be a ..... : she's the mother of my brother-in-law's wife.

9 Complete the phrasal verbs. Choose the correct option.

1 I used to hang *out with / around* John a lot at college because we were both keen swimmers.

2 I'm meeting *with / up with* a group of colleagues on Friday. Would you like to join us?

3 I don't get *off / on* very well with my new boss. He's really difficult to work with.

4 Do you want to come *across / round* to my house and watch the football? It starts at 8 p.m.

5 It's very important to stand *by / with* your friends when they are in trouble.

6 Some people are very good at keeping *up with / on with* their old friends. I've lost touch with practically all the people I knew at college.

7 Jane and I were friends at school, but when we met we just seemed to pick *off / up* from where we left off 20 years ago.

8 It's your 30th birthday next month. What kind of celebration are you going *for / after*?

1b Young and old

Listening the ageing population

1 1.1 Listen to an extract from a radio programme about the ageing population. Are the sentences true (T) or false (F)?

1 People are not having so many children as in the past.
2 People don't eat and exercise as healthily as in the past.
3 Older people are not as much at risk from deadly diseases as they were in the past.
4 The average age that anyone in the world can expect to live to is now around 80.
5 In the future, the money to support the old will come from the younger generation.
6 The ageing population will help bring families closer together.

2 1.1 Complete the sentences with nouns. Then listen to the programme again and check.

Reasons for the ageing population

1 The birth ..... has declined over the last 20 years.
2 60 years ago, there was a baby ..... ; these 'baby boomers' are now reaching ..... age.
3 Improved ..... : people eat more healthily these days.
4 Healthier ..... : not only do people eat better, they are also more aware of the need to keep fit.
5 Advances in medicine have increased life ..... to around 80 in the developed world.
6 People are given routine ..... against life-threatening diseases, e.g. flu jabs for the elderly.

Grammar the passive

3 Rewrite the sentences from the active to the passive form.

1 Governments **are forcing** people to work longer.
People ..... to work longer.
2 Governments **have raised** the age of retirement in many countries.
The age of retirement ..... in many countries.
3 People **don't consider** someone to be old until they are about 80.
Someone ..... to be old until they are about 80.
4 The government **is encouraging** each family to have more children.
Each family ..... to have more children.
5 The government **reduces** taxes for families with more than two children.
Taxes ..... for families with more than two children.
6 The public **have not welcomed** the idea of working longer for less money.
The idea of working longer for less money ..... by the public.

4 Look at these sentences from the radio programme. Complete the sentences with the passive form of the verbs.

1 More ..... (know) these days about healthy and unhealthy eating.
2 Food producers ..... (oblige) to give consumers more information about the salt and fat content of their food.
3 In the past few years, people ..... (educate) in the right way to exercise and keep fit.
4 Enormous progress ..... (make) in recent years in the field of medicine.
5 People ..... (also / give) routine vaccinations against diseases like flu.
6 The younger generation ..... (now / outnumber) by the old.

5 Choose the correct option.

1 Life expectancy *is rising / is being risen* in many countries.
2 In the Middle East, the number of young people *is growing / is being grown.*
3 The idea of working longer *has not received / has not been received* well by people.
4 Some people say that advances in medicine *have gone / have been gone* too far.
5 It is unfair that young people *oblige / are obliged* to pay for the care of the old.
6 In some western countries, people *encouraging / are being encouraged* to have more children.

6 Pronunciation weak forms in passive verbs

a 1.2 Listen to the sentences. Which parts of the verb in bold are NOT stressed? Circle the unstressed word.

1 People **are given** better protection against deadly diseases.
2 Some great advances **have been made** in medical science.
3 The problem of the ageing population **is being discussed** by many governments.
4 A satisfactory solution to this problem **has not yet been found**.
5 Working longer **is considered** to be one solution.
6 People **are expected** to work longer than in the past.

b 1.3 It is possible to stress auxiliary verbs for emphasis. Listen to the phrases. Are the underlined words stressed (S) or unstressed/weak form (W)?

	S	W
1 He <u>has been</u> told several times.	☐	☐
2 You <u>are</u> not allowed to smoke.	☐	☐
3 I <u>have been</u> given a new job.	☐	☐
4 She <u>is being</u> educated at home.	☐	☐
5 They <u>are</u> looked after very well.	☐	☐
6 The questions <u>are being</u> discussed.	☐	☐

7 Dictation old and young

1.4 Look at the photo. The person is describing her family. Listen and write what she says. What is she looking forward to when she is older?

1 I think my parents' generation .....
.....
2 My parents ..... , but they both .....
..... . So now they can relax and enjoy themselves.
3 They've said .....
.....
and that we children .....
.....
4 Considering that my husband and I
.....
.....
.....

1c A dynamic society

Listening a study project in Vietnam

1 1.5 Listen to an interview with a student who recently returned from a study trip to Vietnam. Which statement (a–c) best summarises her views about the different generations in Vietnamese society?

a There is a deep cultural divide between the old and the young generations.
b All generations are confused by the changes taking place.
c The generations see things differently, but they all respect each other.

2 1.5 Listen to the interview again. Are the sentences true (T) or false (F)?

1 Both the presenter and Lauren went on study trips as part of their university courses.
2 Vietnam is in a period of great economic and social change.
3 Lauren had the opportunity to meet a lot of ordinary Vietnamese citizens.
4 The older generation has suffered to reach where they are now.
5 Younger people are a little nervous about greater contact with the outside world.
6 The Vietnamese think it's very important to teach the young about the country's history.
7 Lauren felt that the different generations in the family couldn't understand each other.
8 The older generation is increasingly ignored by younger people.

3 Look at the phrases in bold from the interview. Choose the correct definition (a–c).

1 We were lucky to experience that **first-hand** …
a for ourselves
b for the first time
c something no one else has ever experienced

2 We **got to** meet …
a had the opportunity to meet
b were obliged to meet
c met by chance

3 They **take** this new wealth **for granted** …
a are suspicious of it
b are grateful for it
c assume it should be like this

4 They don't know **which way to turn** …
a the rules
b what to do
c where to drive

5 The generation in the middle **bridges the gap** …
a creates a space between two things
b joins two sides
c crosses from one side to another

6 The **30-somethings** …
a the 1930s
b a group of 30 objects
c people in their 30s

4 **Pronunciation word stress: *-ic* and *-tion/-sion***

a 1.6 Listen to these words from the interview. Underline the stressed syllable in each word. What pronunciation rule can you make about words that end in *-ic* and *-tion*?

1 dynamic	4 generation
2 fantastic	5 restriction
3 economics	6 tradition

Rule: .....

b 1.7 Practise saying these words, putting the stress on the correct syllable. Then listen and check.

specific	impression
italics	relation
terrific	interruption
scientific	transformation
characteristic	comprehension

1d What a nice surprise!

Real life meeting people you know

1 Look at the sentences. Some prepositions are missing. Insert the correct preposition, where necessary.

1 Fancy bumping ..... you here!
2 How's it all going .....?
3 What have you been up ..... lately?
4 I've been completely snowed ..... with work.
5 Being self-employed obviously suits ..... you.
6 Do you see much ..... Georgia these days?
7 How is your daughter getting ..... at university?
8 Do give ..... them my regards.
9 I'm ..... a bit of a hurry.
10 Good luck ..... the new job.

2 Grammar extra present perfect: simple and continuous

Look at the highlighted verbs in the sentences (1–4). Are they in the present perfect simple (PPS) or present perfect continuous (PPC) form?

1 He**'s moved** to New York for his job. .....
2 What **have you been doing** since I last saw you? .....
3 I **haven't seen** Hannah for ages. .....
4 She**'s been preparing** for her law exams. .....

3 Look at the sentences in Exercise 2 again. Answer the questions.

1 Which tense emphasises how someone has spent their time recently? .....
2 Which tense emphasises a present result? .....

4 Read the conversation. Choose the correct option.

Ben: Hi Sam. [a] ..... .
I've [1] *wondered / been wondering* how you were.
Sam: Oh, hi Ben. [b] ..... .
I'm fine. I've [2] *worked / been working* in Scotland for the last three months.
Ben: Well, [c] ..... .
You're looking very well. Have you [3] *decided / been deciding* to move up there?
Sam: No, it's just a temporary job. I've [4] *helped / been helping* to renovate an old castle. And [d] ..... ? Is Emily well?
Ben: Yes, thanks. She's just [5] *finished / been finishing* her nursing course.
Sam: Really? That's fantastic. [e] ..... .
Ben: Well, [f] ..... .
I should probably go and do my shopping.
Sam: OK. Could I have your phone number again? I've [6] *lost / been losing* it.
Ben: Sure. It's 07945 699636.
Sam: Thanks. Well, speak soon, I hope. [g] ..... .

5 1.8 Listen to the conversation in Exercise 4. Complete the phrases (a–g).

6 Pronunciation expressive intonation

1.9 Look at the phrases (1–6). Would you say them with an expressive intonation (E) or a flatter intonation (F)? Then listen and check.

	E	F
1 What a nice surprise.	☐	☐
2 Busy as ever.	☐	☐
3 How are things?	☐	☐
4 You're looking well.	☐	☐
5 Say hello to her from me.	☐	☐
6 Great to see you.	☐	☐

7 Listen and respond meeting people you know

1.10 Listen to comments where someone meets a friend by chance in the street. Respond with your own words. Then compare your response with the model answer that follows.

1 *Hi. What a nice surprise! How are you?*

I'm fine, thanks. Good to see you.

1e News from home

Writing an informal email

1 Complete the email to a friend who is working abroad. Use the sentences and phrases (a–g).

a So keep your fingers crossed for me.
b All the best,
c How are you **getting on**?
d Anyway, do send me your news when you **get** a moment to write.
e What news from here?
f I'm sorry I haven't written sooner.
g Dear Esther

1 .....
2 ..... I hope everything is going OK. 3 ..... I've been really busy at work the last few weeks. Everyone has been asking about you. How is your Arabic coming on? I imagine you're able to **get by** with day-to-day conversations by now. 4 ..... Well, shortly after you left, I **got** a letter from a fashion designer in New York. They saw some of my work in a catalogue for the shop that I work for and they want me to fly over to New York for an interview. I'm trying not to **get** too excited about it in case they don't offer me a job, but as you know, it's always been my dream to get a job with a top designer.
5 .....
The other big piece of news is that Sarah is going to **get** married next year! I've met her boyfriend and he seems a really nice guy. They've fixed the date for 9th July. I hope you'll be back by then.
6 .....
It'd be great to hear how things are there.
7 .....
Sophie

Word focus *get*

2 Look at the verb *get* highlighted in the email in Exercise 1, either on its own or as part of a phrasal verb. Match the uses of *get* to a word with a similar meaning in the box.

be become doing have manage obtain received

....
....
....
.....

3 Look at the verb *get* in these sentences. Write a synonym for *get* in each sentence.

1 I'm sorry. I don't **get** what you're saying. Why do I have to wait? .....
2 Can you **get off** the phone? I'm trying to work. .....
3 I **got** this jacket for £20 in the sales. .....
4 Call me when you **get to** the station. .....
5 We had to **get** a taxi because there were no buses. .....
6 It was a bad cold. It took me two weeks to **get over** it. .....
7 They **got** first prize in the dancing competition. .....
8 Could you **get** the map from the car so that we can plan our route? .....

4 Rewrite this informal email.

1 First write the verbs in the correct tense.
2 Then see how many verbs you can replace with *get*.

Dear Jack,
I 1 ..... (receive) your email yesterday.
I 2 ..... (be) glad that you 3 ..... (arrive) there safely. It 4 ..... (sound) as if you 5 ..... (have) a really busy time.
Sorry to hear that you 6 ..... (be) delayed at the airport in the UK. I 7 ..... (hope) you 8 ..... (recover) now from the long journey to Chennai.
I hope the weather 9 ..... (not/become) any hotter too – 45 degrees Centigrade 10 ..... (sound) quite enough! I 11 ..... (not/think) I 12 ..... (ever/experience) temperatures like that.
Nothing much 13 ..... (happen) here since you left. I 14 ..... (try) to find a new job, but I 15 ..... (not/be) able to find anything suitable yet. I'll let you know when I 16 ..... (find) one.
Louis 17 ..... (help) me to write a CV and a covering letter, because I 18 ..... (not/really/understand) the whole job application process.
Anyway, fingers crossed.
Good luck with everything there and write again soon.
Love,
Theresa

Wordbuilding forming adjectives from nouns

1 Complete the table. Form adjectives from the nouns and verbs below.

~~care~~ conservation control child decision ~~depend~~ difference dominate ~~entrepreneur~~ ~~fool~~ help humour industry intellect self love play practice ~~respect~~ ~~sense~~ ~~study~~

-ful	-ish	-ive	-ious/-ous	-ent/-ant	-al	-ing
respectful	*foolish*	*sensitive*	*studious*	*dependent*	*entrepreneurial*	*caring*
.....	.....	.....	.....	.....	.....	.....
.....	.....	.....	.....	.....	.....	.....

2 Complete this interview about a family using adjectives from Exercise 1.

Are you a close family?
Yes, we are. We all have our own lives and careers so we are not [1] ..... on each other, but we remain very close.

Why do you think that is?
We were brought up in a very [2] ..... and loving environment and taught to look after each other.

Is there a clear head of the family?
It's quite a [3] ..... and traditional family in many ways. My father is certainly the [4] ..... figure – he gives the orders.

And do you all share a particular family trait?
We're all quite [5] ..... and down-to-earth people: good with our hands

Is there someone in the family you admire especially?
My uncle, who's a historian. He's more [6] ..... and quite a deep thinker, but he can also be very [7] ..... . He tells some very funny stories.

Has your family influenced your own path in life?
Yes. My father is an inventor and I think I have inherited his [8] ..... spirit. I set up my own business when I was 22. He's also very hard-working and we are [9] ..... types too.

Learning skills extending your vocabulary

3 You can extend your vocabulary by making word families. Look at the word *decide*. How many words can you think of that are related to it? Complete the words and expressions.

- different parts of speech: *decision* (noun), *decisive* (adjective), [1] ..... (adverb)
- collocations: *make a decision*, [2] ..... *a decision*
- opposites: *indecision*, [3] .....
- synonyms: *make up your mind*, *come to a* [4] .....

4 Now write a word family for another word. Choose two from the list.

fortune immigration influence obey respect support

Check!

5 Do the quiz. Choose the correct option. All answers appear in Student's Book Unit 1.

1 Orang-utans are unusual in that they like to … .
   a spend time with other animals
   b share their food
   c live independently

2 A fair-weather friend is someone who … .
   a helps you in difficult situations
   b makes a bad situation better
   c is only a friend in good times

3 In which passive sentence is there NO agent?
   a Bella has been raised in China.
   b The right brands are selected by Bella.
   c Her parents are confused by all the changes taking place in China.

4 The adjective from the noun *rebel* is … .
   a rebelful b rebellient c rebellious

5 An expression for saying you are overloaded with work is to be … .
   a snowed up
   b snowed in
   c snowed under

Unit 2 Storytelling

2a March of the Penguins

Reading a film documentary

1 Read the interview with a film director and answer the questions.

1 What is unusual about the lives of the penguins?

.....

.....

2 What is the theme of the film?

.....

Glossary
breed (v) /briːd/ have children
hatch (v) /hætʃ/ be born from an egg
chick (n) /tʃɪk/ a baby bird

2 Read the interview again and choose the correct option to complete the sentences.

1 The penguins make the long journey across Antarctica to *find food / have chicks*.
2 The mother penguins must hurry back from the ocean to feed *their young / the males*.
3 The director thinks the penguins' story was suited to film because it is *dramatic / romantic*.
4 It was easy to film the penguins because they are *friendly / predictable*.
5 The interviewer is surprised that the penguins can survive *out of water / in such hard conditions*.

Stefan Lovgren for National Geographic News

March of the Penguins tells the remarkable story of emperor penguins who each year journey for hundreds of miles across the ice of Antarctica to reach their traditional breeding ground. After laying a single egg, the females return to the ocean for fish, leaving the males behind to guard the eggs, which they balance on top of their feet, even during snowstorms. After two months, during which the males eat nothing, the eggs begin to hatch. But if the mothers are late returning from the ocean with food, the chicks will die. French director Luc Jacquet spoke to us about the challenges of making *March of the Penguins*.

Your background is as a biologist. How did you become interested in penguins?
In 1992, I spent fourteen months at the French scientific centre in Antarctica doing research. In my career, I have also worked as a cameraman. I helped to shoot another film, *The Congress of the Penguins*, in 1995. I was also inspired by the sheer beauty of Antarctica, and I felt this was a great story for the movies. It has all the elements of great drama – love, life, death.

In the film, the narration comes from the penguins' perspective – we hear their thoughts. Why did you choose this storytelling technique?
I wanted to get away from the documentary genre and to write a story that made the viewer feel like he or she was really right there with the penguins.

How did you approach the penguins?
It was easy to get near them. They have never experienced any form of colonisation, so they're not scared of humans. They are also easy to work with because it's possible to anticipate everything they do – the route they will take, or how they will act in any given situation.

How would you describe the overall theme of the movie?
I wanted to tell things as I felt them, rather than as a scientist. It's about the struggle between life and death. The penguins have learned to live where no other creature can. This is what struck me the most. How do they do that? How do they manage?

The penguins are bad walkers. How did nature allow them to make this terrible trek across the ice?
That's a good question, and I haven't found an answer for it. But I think if you gave the penguins the option of spending all their lives underwater, they would take it.

3 Look at the interview again. Find words that mean:

1 to film .....
2 motivated .....
3 a type of film .....
4 to predict .....
5 made an impression on .....

Grammar past simple and present perfect

4 Look at the film-maker's answers in the interview. Find examples of the following:

1 his experience in general (present perfect)
.....
2 something he did at a specific time in the past (past simple) .....
3 something the penguins did in the past that has a present result (present perfect)
.....

5 Complete the final part of the interview using the verbs in the present perfect simple and past simple forms.

Some would say you have to be crazy to spend more than a year in such an inhospitable environment.

I [1] ..... (met) many explorers and adventurers in my life. Some of them [2] ..... (spend) their careers climbing mountains, others like to cross the desert or the sea. I [3] ..... (always / feel) comfortable in the polar environment. On this visit, I [4] ..... (get) a particular sense of adventure. Yes, I [5] ..... (encounter) a lot of difficulties. But once I had been there for a while, my body [6] ..... (adapt) to the environment. Over time, I [7] ..... (learn) to deal with the terrific wind, which in some ways is worse than the cold temperatures. Everyone who [8] ..... (visit) the polar regions for any length of time will tell you this. What you have to do is to learn to minimise body movement. So I [9] ..... (not / run) anywhere when I was there. I just [10] ..... (do) everything carefully and slowly.

Vocabulary books and films

6 Complete the review of *March of the Penguins* using these words.

audience	accurate	cast	director
gripping	location	sentimental	scenes
storyline	touching		

The [1] ..... Jacquet has made a visually stunning film. But some people may find his approach to the penguins is too [2] ....., because he has romanticised their story by giving them a human voice.

I found it more [3] ..... than many thrillers, and more [4] ..... than many romantic films. And all without a [5] ..... of human actors.

Filmed on [6] ..... in Antarctica, *March of the Penguins* paints an [7] ..... picture of how harsh life can be for these creatures. Behind the basic [8] ..... of the struggle for survival is a message for the [9] ..... about modern family life. It contains some extraordinary [10] ....., such as the males protecting their eggs in a raging blizzard.

7 Pronunciation the letter *l*

1.11 Look at these words. Write *S* if you think the letter 'l' is silent. Then listen and check.

1 talk .....
2 silk .....
3 bold .....
4 could .....
5 calf .....
6 installed .....
7 folk .....
8 wild .....
9 calm .....
10 film .....

8 Dictation describing books and films

1.12 Listen to someone describing the book *A week at the Airport*. Complete the sentences.

1 The ..... Alain de Botton's ....., *A Week at the Airport*, is Heathrow airport.
2 The ..... that passes through the airport.
3 The ..... with travellers and airline staff.
4 ..... is that if you are looking for somewhere that ....., you don't need to look any further than an airport.

2b True stories

Listening the Aron Ralston story

1 1.13 Listen to adventurer Aron Ralston's story, which was recently made into the film, *127 Hours*. Which of these sentences summarises what he did?

a When he became trapped, Ralston panicked.
b When he became trapped, Ralston thought carefully about what to do next.
c When he became trapped, Ralston knew immediately what he had to do.

Glossary
boulder (n) /ˈbəʊldə(r)/ a large rock or stone
wedged (adj) /wedʒd/ caught between two surfaces e.g. two walls
multi-tool (n) /ˈmʌltituːl/ a tool like a Swiss army knife
numb (adj) /nʌm/ unable to feel anything

2 1.13 Listen again and choose the best option.

1 Ralston went to Bluejohn Canyon:
a to help prepare himself for a future mountain climb.
b to do some mountain biking.
c to do a bit of camping.

2 His hand became trapped when:
a he stood on one of the boulders.
b he dropped down onto a boulder.
c he put his arm around a boulder.

3 Ralston's options were to:
a wait for help or free his hand.
b wait for help or cut off his hand.
c free his hand or cut off his hand.

4 The first thing he tried was:
a calling for help.
b freeing his hand with his multi-tool.
c chipping away part of his trapped hand.

5 After five days, Ralston finally:
a walked out of the canyon.
b was lifted out of the Canyon by some tourists.
c walked all the way out of the National Park.

3 Look at the verbs in bold. Match the verbs with the correct definition.

1 He **stretched** to reach a secure foothold.
a extended his leg
b stepped
c bent his leg

2 The boulder **slid down** …
a crashed
b slipped
c rolled

3 The boulder trapped his hand, **crushing** it.
a causing it pain
b destroying it with pressure
c cutting it

4 He tried to **shift** the boulder.
a move
b break
c get on top of

5 He **chipped away** at the rock.
a scratched
b rubbed
c broke little pieces off

6 **Dripping** blood, he made his way back.
a letting large amounts escape
b letting drops fall
c trying to stop the flow

Grammar past tenses review

4 Complete the story using the correct past tense form of the verbs in brackets.

On April 25, 2003, Aron Ralston [1] ..... (drive) to Moab, Utah, where he mountain-biked the famous Slickrock Trail. He then [2] ..... (make) his way to Horseshoe Canyon. When he [3] ..... (arrive), night [4] ..... (fall), so he made camp.

He [5] ..... (climb) into the canyon on April 26. He [6] ..... (go) about five miles when he came to a section where a series of large boulders [7] ..... (hang), wedged between the walls of the canyon.

He [8] ..... (not/tell) anyone where he was. It would be days before anyone realised that he was missing. Ralston [9] ..... (stand) on a small stone, facing the boulder that [10] ..... (crush) his hand. The pain was intense, but he was determined to stay in control …

Ralston [11] ..... (wait) there for five days. But by the time the search teams started out, he [12] ..... (already/decide) what he had to do …

5 Look at the sentences. If it got dark at 6.00 p.m., when did Ralston arrive in each case? Match the sentences (1–3) with the times (a–c).

1 When he arrived at Horseshoe Canyon, night fell. .....
2 When he arrived at Horseshoe Canyon, night was falling. .....
3 When he arrived at Horseshoe Canyon, night had fallen. .....

a around 6.00 p.m.
b 6.00 p.m.
c 7.00 p.m.

6 Pronunciation contracted negative forms

1.14 Listen and write down the missing word, either an auxiliary verb or a contracted negative form.

1 I ..... been there before.
2 You ..... allowed to smoke.
3 It ..... the first time this has happened.
4 She ..... the person I told you about.
5 They ..... as tired from the journey as I expected.
6 I ..... talking about what happened to me.
7 She ..... been waiting a long time.
8 I ..... spoken French for years.

7 Grammar extra present tenses for narratives

a Read this short review of the film *127 Hours*, the Aron Ralston story. What tenses are used to describe the plot of the film?

.....

Film title: *127 Hours*
Rating: 8.5
Director: Danny Boyle (*Slumdog Millionaire, Trainspotting*)
Actors: James Franco, Kate Mara, Amber Tamblyn
Genre: Action film
Release date: November 2010
Synopsis: Aron Ralston, a 27-year-old hiker, is canyoneering in Utah's remote Bluejohn Canyon. An 800-pound boulder falls and traps his hand, making it impossible for him to move. He hasn't told anyone where he is going. Based on a true story.

▶ GRAMMAR EXTRA present tenses for narratives

We use present tenses to describe the plot of a book or a film and to review them.
In the film '127 Hours' Aron Ralston is canyoneering in Utah's remote Bluejohn Canyon.
An 800-pound boulder falls and traps his hand.
He hasn't told anyone where he is going.
This use of the present tense is sometimes referred to as 'the present historic'.

b Look at the grammar box. Then complete the synopsis of a book using the verbs in the correct tense.

Book title: *To the Ends of the Earth*
Author: Ranulph Fiennes
Genres: Autobiography; travel; adventure
Synopsis: The mountaineer and explorer Ranulph Fiennes [1] ..... (give) a personal and gripping account of an expedition around the world from top to bottom. The adventures really [2] ..... (begin) once the group [3] ..... (reach) Antarctica and tensions [4] ..... (grow) between the friends, while all the time conditions [5] ..... (get) worse.

2c Children's stories

Listening the stories of Oscar Wilde

1 1.15 Listen to a review of a collection of short stories by Oscar Wilde. Are the sentences true (T) or false (F)?

1 The stories were written for children.
2 The stories were published recently.
3 All the stories reveal something about human behaviour.
4 In the story of the Happy Prince, the statue of the prince can think, feel and speak.
5 The Happy Prince wants to help the little bird.
6 The Happy Prince has a happy ending.

Glossary
ostensibly (adv) /ɒst'ensɪbli/ apparently
swallow (n) /'swɒləʊ/ a kind of bird that migrates
eyesore (n) /'aɪsɔ:(r)/ something unpleasant to look at

2 1.16 Complete the sentences. Then listen again to the first part of the review and check your answers.

1 The stories are suitable for ..... and ..... .
2 They contain elements that you would find in a traditional ..... .
3 At the heart of what makes them beautiful is their ..... .
4 People who read the stories are ..... by them.
5 Oscar Wilde did not like to give ..... .

3 1.17 Read the summary of the story of *The Happy Prince*. Then listen again to the second part of the review and choose the correct option.

The Happy Prince is [1] *an elegant / a shabby* statue in the centre of an old town in northern Europe. Each day the prince [2] *proudly ignores / watches closely* what is happening in the town. One day, [3] *he stops a little swallow / a little swallow stops off with him* on its way to Egypt for the winter. The prince [4] *asks / orders* him to take the gold and jewels from his statue to poor [5] *people / children* around the town. The swallow continues doing this for some [6] *days / weeks*. In the end, the swallow [7] *is exhausted / catches cold* and dies at the foot of the statue. When the town councillors see the statue without its gold and jewels, they decide to [8] *destroy / renovate* it.

Word focus *keep*

4 Look at the phrases with *keep* from the story of *The Happy Prince*. Match the phrases (1–4) with the correct meaning (a–d).

1 I still had to **keep back** the tears.
2 Oscar Wilde **kept from** giving moral lessons.
3 From where he stands, he can **keep abreast of** all that is happening in the town.
4 The swallow stays for some days **keeping** the prince **company**.

a spend time with
b prevent (someone) from doing something
c hold in and not release something
d stay in touch or up-to-date with

5 Complete the sentences using these phrases. You will need to use the correct form. There are two extra phrases.

keep abreast of keep an eye on keep track of
keep (someone) company keep (someone) from
keep back keep a secret keep a promise

1 Thanks for your help and sorry if I ..... your work.
2 Those flowers are a thank you present from Sarah. I ..... her flat while she was away.
3 People visit my grandfather at the weekend, but during the week there is no one to ..... .
4 My brother is travelling around the world and he sends me emails so I can ..... his progress.
5 Apart from a small amount of money that she ..... for emergencies, she spent everything she had saved.
6 It's not fair to ask someone to .... if they know telling it will help someone they know.

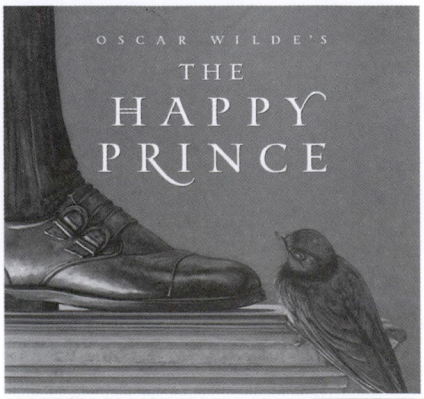

2d I can sympathise

Real life reacting to stories

1 Look at these situations where things have gone wrong. Complete the sentences using the correct form of the verb.

1 My trousers got caught on a nail and ..... (tear).
2 The key ..... (break) in the lock as I was turning it.
3 The boy put his head through the railings and it got ..... (stick).
4 He had ..... (make) a big hole in his jumper.
5 The pipe ..... (freeze) because it was so cold.
6 When it warmed up again, the pipe ..... (burst).

2 Underline the words or phrases that can begin each reaction. Sometimes more than one answer is possible. Then match the reactions to the situations in Exercise 1.

a *How / What a / That was* nightmare!
b *How / What a / That was* good thinking.
c *How / What a / That was* embarrassing.
d *How / What a / That was* lucky.
e *How / Poor / What* a stroke of luck.
f *How / Poor / What* strange.
g *How / Poor / What* you!
h *How / What / That must have been* a relief.
i *How / What / That must have been* awkward.
j *How / What / That must have been* a disaster.

3 1.18 Listen to two friends talking about a travel story. Answer the questions.

1 What was the problem?
out of fuel
2 How did they resolve the problem?
to passport office in London
3 How did the speaker feel by the end of their ordeal?
Very stressed

4 1.18 Listen again. Complete the reactions (1–6). Use phrases a–f.

a How stressful!
b Oh, that's awful.
c I think I would have done the same thing.
d Oh no. Poor you.
e I can sympathise.
f That was a stroke of luck.

1 d What happened?
2 b So did you leave her behind?
3 f And where were you?
4 a Did they make it in time?
5 e I hate being late when I'm travelling.
6 Did you? I don't blame you. c

5 Pronunciation linking and assimilation

a 1.19 The following phrases are either linked (1–4) or assimilated (the last letter of the first word is absorbed into the opening consonant of the second word). Listen and repeat.

1 large area
2 immediate action
3 open air
4 cry out
5 a burst pipe
6 Great Britain
7 hand baggage
8 bus shelter

b 1.20 Now say these expressions. Then listen and check.

1 thick undergrowth
2 West Africa
3 dead end
4 climb up
5 pocket money
6 credit card
7 nice shoes
8 first class

6 Listen and respond reacting to stories

1.21 Listen to five people telling you news. Respond with your own words. Then compare your response with the model answer that follows.

1

You'll never guess what happened to me yesterday on the bus. I started talking to this woman who I thought was Sue, my next-door neighbour, about my problems at work. But it wasn't Sue, it was a complete stranger!

How embarrassing! When did you realise it wasn't Sue?

2e 'Don't move!'

1 Writing skill using descriptive words

a Read this extract from a story and underline all the verbs and expressions that describe how people speak.

'Don't move,' she whispered, 'I think I can see an animal in the bushes.' 'I know,' Dominic replied anxiously. 'I can hear it too.' They stayed where they were, waiting to see what would appear from the bushes. Dominic, who was clearly very frightened, moaned quietly. 'Be quiet,' muttered Cat, 'or you'll attract its attention.' Just then, the branches parted and a tall man in white clothes stepped out into the clearing. 'Hello there!' he cried.

b Match the descriptive verbs (1–7) with the phrases (a–g).

1 he cried	a she said wearily
2 she moaned	b she said complainingly
3 she whispered	c he said loudly
4 he screamed	d he shouted at the top of his voice
5 he muttered	e he said under his breath
6 she sighed	f she said, not enunciating her words
7 she mumbled	g she said softly

2 Writing skill extra punctuation

a Look at the sentences (1–4). Are the statements (a–d) true (T) or false (F)?

1 He said, 'What a surprise!'
2 'I know,' she said, 'that you don't like eating spicy food.'
3 'Do you agree?' he asked.
4 'I don't agree,' he said.

a You must put quotation marks at the beginning and end of each direct quotation.
b Question marks and exclamation marks belonging to the quotation must be inside the quotation marks.
c You always need a comma to separate the verb of saying from the direct quotation.
d If you break a sentence of a direct quotation and insert a verb of saying, you must put a comma after the verb and before the next set of quotation marks.

b Punctuate the following extract from a story with quotation marks and commas where necessary.

I don't think this is going to work Christopher sighed. We've been trying to build this canoe for three days and it still looks like a lump of wood. The wood's too hard he added. Actually, Christopher said Jen encouragingly we are making some progress. What we really need to do is find some better tools. Just then Tom screamed I've got it! Instead of using our penknives directly on the wood, why don't we make some better tools using our knives?

Writing a story

3 Write the opening paragraph of a story about two friends' encounter with a fierce animal. Follow these instructions:

- Begin with the most dramatic point in the narrative.
- Use descriptive verbs of speaking and moving.
- Use some direct speech. Make sure you punctuate it correctly.

Wordbuilding synonyms

1 Make pairs of close synonyms from the following words.

A an author an audience a blockbuster
a cinema to edit a film a hero
to publish a remake a sequel

B a best-seller to cut a follow-up a heroine
a movie a multiplex a novelist
a re-release viewers to release

2 Match words from Exercise 1 with the definitions.

1 a writer of stories .....
2 a leading female character .....
3 people who watch TV .....
4 a very successful book .....
5 to distribute a film for public viewing
.....
6 to remove a scene from a film
.....
7 a book or film that is the next part of the story
.....
8 a cinema with many screens
.....
9 a film which is distributed for a second time
.....
10 an American word for a film
.....

3 Look at these synonyms to do with speaking and movement. Choose the correct definition (a or b) for each.

1 We **trudged** for miles and miles in the baking heat. .....
2 We **stumbled** through the thick undergrowth, desperate to find a path. .....
   a walk almost falling forward
   b walk wearily
3 He **muttered** something about it not being fair.
.....
4 Try not to **mumble**. It's very difficult to hear what you're saying. .....
   a speak indistinctly because you don't want to be heard
   b speak indistinctly
5 She **edged** towards the door and turned the handle slowly. .....
6 She **walked back slowly** to the window and looked out. .....
   a move slowly
   b move slowly and carefully

Learning skills pronunciation

4 Without good pronunciation, people can't understand you. Read these tips to help improve your pronunciation.

1 Don't speak too fast. It's better to be slow and clear than fast and misunderstood.
2 Practise saying phrases and short sentences rather than individual sounds. Listen to native speech and try to imitate the sounds you hear.
3 Record yourself and compare your pronunciation with a native speaker's.
4 Listen to songs in English and imitate exactly what you hear.
5 Practise your pronunciation every day. Choose phrases and texts you have learnt in the unit.

5 Look at these phrases from Unit 2. Follow steps 1–3 in Exercise 4 to practise pronouncing them.

a What a nightmare!
b That must have been a relief.
c I can sympathise with that.

6 Write a mini presentation on a topic of interest to you. Read it aloud and record yourself. Analyse your pronunciation and note your mistakes.

Check!

7 Do the quiz. All the answers are in Student's Book Unit 2.

1 What kind of film or book are these?

a *Senna* .....
b *The Frog Prince* .....
c *The Lord the Rings* .....

2 What were these people's jobs?

a Peter Jackson .....
b Wilhelm Grimm .....
c Steve Winter .....

3 What are these three English idioms?

a a narrow escape = a close .....
b a lucky chance = a ..... of luck
c to get a little exercise = to ..... your legs

3a No magic answer

Reading population growth

1 Read the text about the problem of overpopulation. What does the writer think the solution will be found through?

a technology
b population control
c sharing of resources

2 Read the text and complete the sentences.

1 The problem is not just how many people there are, it's how high their .... is.
2 The economic optimists believe that resources ..... as the population increases.
3 In the last 60 years, food production has grown .... population growth.
4 Parents in under-developed countries need ..... to look after them in their old age.
5 Bill Gates thinks that by improving health in poor countries we can limit population growth by ....
6 For Joel Cohen, there are .... to help solve the problem of overpopulation.

No magic answer

For every problem we always hope there will be a magic answer that will make it go away. That's human nature. But problems like overpopulation are complex and demand complex solutions. First, let's outline a few basic facts.

Firstly, each person on the planet takes up space, consumes resources and creates waste. So the more people there are, the greater the problems of dwindling resources, overcrowding and pollution are going to be.

Secondly, rising standards of living – a product of economic growth – have exactly the same effects. Rich people have bigger houses, buy more consumer goods and generate more waste. So even if the population remains the same, economic growth will create similar problems.

But economic optimists don't worry about an increasing population because, according to them, people don't deplete resources, they create them. For them, more people mean more human intelligence and more brains to find clever ways to boost resources. One example they give is the 'Green Revolution'. Over the last 60 years, agricultural food production has grown dramatically – faster than the population, in fact. Through the engineering of better seeds and plants, which are more resistant to disease, experts predict that there will be enough food for all of us in the future.

Another example is the Gates Foundation's work in combating disease in poor countries through a programme of vaccination. You would think that saving lives through vaccination would actually increase the population, not decrease it. Parents in under-developed countries want to ensure that at least two children will be around to look after them when they are old. So they raise this probability by having more children. However, research shows that when you improve health in such communities, the population growth rate will fall within half a generation. Bill Gates believes that if we continue this work, the world population will peak at 8.3 billion by 2050 rather than the 9.3 billion currently predicted.

But of course technology alone is the not answer. It will help us to protect current resources and to find new resources, but we will also need to look at how we share these. Joel Cohen, a professor at Rockefeller University, put it nicely. He said that three schools of thought had a role to play in lessening the negative effects of overpopulation:

- 'The bigger pie school', who say that technology will increase resources.
- 'The fewer forks school', who say we need to reduce population growth and consumption.
- 'The better manners school', who say we should all share resources more equally.

The last, and probably the real answer, requires a different kind of faith: not in science, but in human nature.

Vocabulary verbs describing trends

3 Find verbs in the passage that describe things getting greater or smaller.

Greater	Smaller
1 r	7 d .....
2 b	8 d .....
3 g	9 d .....
4 i	10 f .....
5 r	11 l .....
6 p	12 r .....

4 Complete the sentences using an appropriate verb from Exercise 3. There is more than one possible answer for some of the sentences.

1 The author thinks that one way or another, we need to ..... the amount of resources we use.
2 The world's population is expected to continue to ..... until around 2050.
3 After that it will probably begin to ..... .
4 The economic optimists believe that whatever problems overpopulation causes, we will find a technological solution to ..... their impact.
5 One way to ..... the chance of having more children who will survive is simply to have more children in the first place.
6 Another way is to ..... the amount of money invested in health programmes in poor countries.

Grammar future forms review

5 Read these comments about the views expressed in the article. Choose the correct option.

1 'Bill Gates argues that if you improve health, people *will have / are having* fewer children. But what he doesn't say is that the result *will be / is about to be* more and more old people.'
2 'If we *will rely / are going to rely* on new technology to solve this problem, then heaven help us. New technology creates as many problems as it solves.'
3 '*I'll tell / I'm going to tell* you something – *I will be / I'm going to be* very surprised if the population growth rate *won't start / doesn't start* to fall in the next 20 years.'
4 'I'm from what the article calls "the better manners school". There are enough resources for everyone, but we *won't solve / don't solve* the problem until we *will share / share* them more equally.'
5 'I'm suspicious of people like Bill Gates. He made a fortune out of business and now he *will save / is going to save* the world.'
6 'Actually, *I'll go / I'm going* to hear Bill Gates speak at a climate change conference this week. It *will begin / begins* on Friday.'

6 Read the conversation about plans to attend a conference. Complete the sentences using the appropriate future form of the verbs.

Phil: Hi, Anna. [1] ..... (you / go) to the 'Future Foods Fair' next weekend?
Anna: Yes, I am. How [2] ..... (you / get) there?
Phil: I [3] ..... (probably / drive). What about you?
Anna: I haven't decided. Perhaps I [4] ..... (go) by train.
Phil: Don't do that – it's so expensive. I [5] ..... (give) you a lift.
Anna: That would be great. What time [6] ..... (you / leave)?
Phil: Well, the conference [7] ..... (start) at 10, so I thought about 8.30.
Anna: That sounds perfect. Do you imagine it [8] ..... (finish) by 6?
Phil: I hope so. I need to be back by 7.30.

7 **Pronunciation /r/ and /t/ in American English**

1.22 Listen to an American speaking about Bill Gates and other philanthropists. Complete the text.

There's a group of philanthropists in the US – Gates, Buffet, Rockefeller, [1] ..... – who have [2] ..... a [3] ..... of money to good causes over the last [4] ..... [5] ..... .
The problem for them is that, because they're so rich and [6] ..... , people get suspicious of their [7] ..... . So when they [8] ..... up, they often do so [9] ..... , like they did a few years ago in [10] ..... .

3b Smart technology

Listening homes of the future

1 1.23 You are going to listen to an interview with a researcher about smart homes of the future. Tick (✓) the items you think you will hear. Then listen and check.

kitchens gadgets	☑	visual media	☑
water use	☑	security	☐
GPS systems	☐	lighting	☑
sound-proofing	☑	hot water systems	☐

2 1.23 Listen again and choose the best option (a–c).

1 The aim of the radio programme is to find out which technology … .
   a is going to be of practical use to us in the near future
   b is the most imaginative
   c will help us to be more environmentally-friendly

2 Intelligent fridges will be more popular when … .
   a they have been developed more
   b they can tell you about the condition of your food
   c they are less expensive

3 Ultrasonic showers are not likely to be used soon because … .
   a sonic waves do not clean the body particularly well
   b we still have plenty of water
   c they could be dangerous

4 The researcher thinks that in the future we could sound-proof rooms using … .
   a magnetic fields
   b high-tech insulation materials
   c energy fields

5 Which of the following will we NOT be able to do with a kitchen surface in the future?
   a watch TV
   b defrost a pizza
   c clean it by hand

6 In the future, we will be using electric lighting in our homes … .
   a in place of natural light
   b to simulate natural light
   c to help control our moods

3 Look at the words and expressions from the interview. Match the words or expressions in bold (1–8) with the correct definition (a–h).

b 1 new **gadgets**	a people who love technology
g 2 just a **gimmick**	b clever devices
a 3 **techies**	c distant
f 4 a **pipe dream**	d imitate or copy
h 5 remains to be **proven**	e protected from
c 6 a **remote** possibility	f fantasy
e 7 sound-**proof**	g thing that simply attracts attention
d 8 **simulate** the sunrise	h shown to be true

Grammar future continuous and future perfect simple

4 Read the sentences and choose the correct option.

1 In a few years, I'm sure we *will be hearing / will have heard* a lot more about this technology.
2 In the future, cookers *will be making / will have made* our meals for us.
3 We *will all be using / will all have used* intelligent fridges when food packaging is intelligent too.
4 In the next ten years, lack of water *will be becoming / will have become* a big issue, so we need to find alternatives.
5 In the future, people *will be using / will have used* energy fields that isolate a particular space from the rest of the house.
6 I don't think people *will be cleaning / will have cleaned* kitchen surfaces either in the future.
7 Soon, we *will be installing / will have installed* surfaces that can act as computer or TV screens in almost every room.
8 I think in ten years or so, that kind of technology *will be becoming / will have become* quite common in new-build houses.
9 Next year, our company *will be launching / will have launched* a new lighting system for bedrooms that simulates the sunrise.

5 Complete these predictions about the use of robots in the home of the future. Put the verbs into the future continuous or future perfect.

When people say that in the future robots [1] ..... (do) all the boring chores around the home, most of us have an image of a human-shaped robot with a feather duster in its hand, which [2] ..... (clean) the house while we sit with our feet up watching TV.

But if you move forward ten years, that is not actually the way technology [3] ..... (develop). In the future, robots in the home will take many forms. Vacuum cleaners that move around the room on their own are already available. In the future, we will see a lot micro-robots, which [4] ..... (do) the kind of jobs that we tend not to do regularly. When we arrive home, micro robots [5] ..... (be) busy all day organising items in our cupboards or cleaning our drains. These robots will already be an integral part of the equipment we use: the fridge, kitchen sink, cupboard, etc. We [6] ..... (not / acquire) them as separate items.

Vocabulary information technology

6 Match the nouns to make collocations.

age	games	graphics	overload
programmer	security	storage	technology

1 information .....
.....

2 data .....
.....

3 computer .....
.....

7 Complete the sentences using one of the noun-noun collocations in Exercise 6.

1 The most serious issue of the next twenty years will be ..... : how we protect our personal and private information.
2 This post-industrial era that we now live in is called the ..... .
3 Augmented reality means projecting ..... onto our view of the real world.
4 Bigger ..... capacity means that portable devices can hold much more information than in the past.
5 People complain that we now have ..... . In other words, there is more information than we can absorb.

8 **Dictation information overload**

1.24 Listen to three facts about the amount of information in the world. Write down the words you hear. Which fact surprised you most?

1 The weekday edition .....
.....
.....
.....

2 Around a thousand .....
.....
.....
.....

3 More information has .....
.....
.....
.....

3c The simplest ideas are the best

Listening lifestraw

1 1.25 Listen to a description of a device called *Lifestraw* and choose the best option (a–c).

1 *Lifestraw* protects against:
   a all stomach infections.
   b certain deadly diseases.
   c 90% of all bacteria.

2 It is operated:
   a with a pump.
   b with a small motor.
   c by sucking.

3 In order to get the best out of it, users need:
   a no training.
   b a day's training.
   c a little advice.

4 It does not solve the problem of:
   a purifying salt water.
   b travelling to get water.
   c drinking dirty water.

2 1.25 Listen again and complete the sentences. Use numbers and figures.

1 In _____, the number of deaths from unclean water was _____ per day.
2 The filter traps _____ of water-borne bacteria.
3 The textile filters stop any particle bigger than _____ microns.
4 Each straw has a cleaning capacity of _____ litres of water.
5 The straw is _____ cm long.
6 Straws were used successfully in Haiti and Pakistan in _____.

3 1.25 Complete these facts about *Lifestraw*. Use the correct verb. Then listen and check.

1 *Lifestraw* _____ on a very simple principle.
2 It _____ protection against the killer diseases cholera and typhoid.
3 The filter _____ a substance called PuroTech Disinfecting Resin.
4 Each filter _____ up to a year.
5 It _____ very little, so it can be worn around the neck.
6 Each device _____ around US $6.
7 It doesn't _____ on electrical power.

4 Pronunciation *dis-, dys-* and *di-*

a 1.26 Listen to these words. Is the underlined letter in each word pronounced /ɪ/ or /aɪ/?

	/ɪ/	/aɪ/
1 disaster	☐	☐
2 dysentry	☐	☐
3 diarrhoea	☐	☐
4 disease	☐	☐
5 diagram	☐	☐

b 1.27 Practise saying these words. Then listen and check.

diabetes discomfort dysfunctional
distance diamond distribution
diary dyslexic disabled diagonal

Vocabulary useful devices

5 Complete these sentences. The first letter has been given for you.

1 *Lifestraw* offers a n_____ solution to a serious, complicated problem.
2 Because you don't need to learn how to use it, it's an excellent example of a _____ technology.
3 For many people in developing countries, collecting water is a very time-c_____ process.
4 *Lifestraw's* appeal is that it's a very h_____ gadget – portable, useful and easy to operate.
5 Although it is simple for the user, inside it uses c_____ edge technology to filter out bacteria.
6 WaterAid is worried that *Lifestraw* is a quick f_____ for a more complex problem.

3d Computers

Vocabulary computing

1 Look at the icons. Match the words with the icons.

attach copy cut format highlight open
paste save search select sort undo

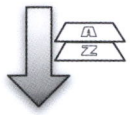
1 .....

2 .....

3 .....

4 .....

5 .....

6 .....

7 .....

8 .....

9 .....

10 .....

11 .....

12 .....

Real life asking for and offering help

2 1.28 Listen to a conversation about a computer problem. Answer the questions.

1 What is the problem?

.....

.....

2 What are the two possible solutions?
1 .....
2 .....

3 Why doesn't the first speaker like the first solution?

.....

.....

3 1.28 Complete the conversation. Use one word in each space. Then listen and check your answers.

Andy: Can you [1] ..... me a [2] ..... ? I'm having [3] ..... sending this document.

Meg: What do you want to do [4] ..... ?

Andy: Nothing very complicated. I'm [5] ..... to attach this document to an email and it won't let me.

Meg: [6] ..... me have a [7] ..... . OK, I see – the document's too large.

Andy: The [8] ..... is it's got a lot of photos in it, and I can't just cut them.

Meg: No, well you [9] ..... compress the photos.

Andy: What does that [10] ..... ?

Meg: I'll [11] ..... you. Right-click on the photo … If you do that with all of them, that should do the [12] ..... .

Andy: Yes, I [13] ..... , but then that reduces the quality of the photos. What [14] ..... do you suggest?

Meg: Have you [15] ..... dividing the document into three or four separate documents?

Andy: No, I'll give that a [16] ..... and see if it [17] ..... .

Meg: OK. Feel [18] ..... to ask if you want me to help you compress the photos after all.

4 **Pronunciation stress in two syllable verbs**

1.29 In two syllable verbs, the stress usually falls on the second syllable. Listen and find the two words that do not fit this stress pattern.

attach compress control divide highlight
involve open prepare reduce select suggest

5 **Listen and respond asking for and offering technical help**

1.30 Listen to someone asking a friend for help with a computer problem. Respond with your own words. Then compare your response with the model answer that follows.

1

Can you help me? My presentation slides look really boring!

OK. What do you want to do exactly?

3e a technical problem

1 Writing skill being polite

Rewrite the sentences so that they are more polite. Use the bold words.

1 Is it OK if I bring your memory stick back on my way home from work tonight?
please _____ ?

2 Where can I find a battery charger for my old phone?
happen _____ ?

3 I want you to send a brochure for your air conditioning units.
could _____ ?

4 What is the phone number for Apricot Computers? I can't find it anywhere.
know _____ ?

5 I want to know how to download photos from my X306 camera.
advise _____ ?

6 What about reducing the price?
able _____ ?

7 I need you to come over and fix my internet connection.
mind _____ ?

8 What number should I call to get technical advice?
tell _____ ?

Word focus *out of*

2 Complete the phrases with *out of* in these answers using the words below.

business	date	depth	interest
luck	order	question	way

a Sorry, I'm a bit out of my _____ there. I know about computers but not telephone connections.

b I regret to say that a discount is out of the _____.

c Unfortunately, that's because they went out of _____ years ago.

d I'm afraid it's so out of _____ that probably no one stocks them anymore.

e I'm afraid our phone system is out of _____ at the moment. Please email me your number and we will call you back asap.

f Thank you, but please don't go out of your _____.

g I will put one in the post to you today. Just out of _____, where did you hear about our company?

h I'm afraid you are out of _____ there. We don't deal with the X306 range.

3 Match the requests (1–8) in Exercise 1 with the responses (a–h) in Exercise 2.

Writing short email requests

4 Write a short email to a friend about a problem you have with your computer. Use the notes below and polite requests.

- tried to call – no answer
- computer keeps crashing
- same problem you had?
- please email instructions to my work email about virus removal
- or call me

Wordbuilding prefixes

1 Match each prefix in box A to at least two words in box B to form words.

A bio hyper mega micro semi ultra

B byte chip conscious detached degradable diversity market sensitive sonic star violet wave

2 Which word is used to describe:

1 a very large shop? .....
2 a piece of cooking equipment? .....
3 a unit of computer memory? .....
4 a range of different plants and animals? .....
5 a piece of silicon with an electric circuit printed on it? .....
6 a house with another house attached on one side? .....
7 someone who is abnormally sensitive? .....
8 a kind of light? .....
9 above the range of human hearing? .....
10 a very famous entertainer? .....
11 non-polluting? .....
12 not fully awake or aware? .....

Wordbuilding compound nouns (noun + noun)

3 Match a noun from box A with a noun from box B and write the collocations.

A address battery credit data information news repair travel

B life manual protection card technology book story advice

....
....
....
....

Learning skills personalising new language

4 The best way to remember something is to make it relevant to you. Read the tips and answer the questions.

Grammar

Think about the grammar in this unit. Write sentences about:

a where you are going to go on holiday next year.
b what you are doing at the weekend.
c what your next career step is going to be.
d which person in your family will be the next to get married.
e what you will be doing in five years' time.
f what you hope you will have achieved in ten years' time.

Vocabulary

a Find four words from Unit 3 that relate to your life. What is their relevance?
b Think, in your own language, about your own predictions for future technology. Can you translate all the terms you used? If not, look up the missing words in a dictionary.

Pronunciation

Think about any words in this unit that you found difficult to pronounce.

a What were they?
b Do they remind you of any words in your own language?
c How do they sound different?

Writing

Think of something you really need some help with. Write a short email request in English to a friend asking for their help.

Check!

5 Complete the sentences. Then use the first letter of each word to make another word, which describes the problems in Student's Book Unit 3a. All the answers are in Student's Book Unit 3.

1 Another word for a device or tool is a ..... . (5)
2 Thomas Malthus said that people were 'basically ..... '. (4)
3 In today's multi-media world, we all suffer from 'information ..... '. (8)
4 A great scientific advance is often called a technological ..... . (12)
5 ' ..... technology' provides the simplest and best solution to a problem. (11)
6 If you miss the opportunity to get something, you are 'out of ..... '. (4)

Word: .....

Unit 4 Art and creativity

4a What's on in London?

Vocabulary performance

1 Complete the sentences using the correct words.

act band company exhibition gallery
gig musical performance play show
theatre venue

1 We saw a great _____ last week. It was a kind of variety performance with different performers. The best one was a circus _____ who did some amazing tricks on a high wire.

2 I went to a _____ at that new music _____ on the High Street last night. It was a local jazz _____ called 'Take Two Project'. They were very professional, I thought.

3 Have you seen the photography _____ at the Oxford Art _____? There are some amazing pictures in it.

4 My daughter has joined a dance _____ who are going to go on tour next month. Their first _____ will be at the new _____ in the centre of town.

5 You know the _____ Macbeth by William Shakespeare. Well, the Victoria Drama Company have turned it into a _____, with singing and dancing.

What's on in London?

1 The Alternative Village Fete

This fete at the National Theatre Square on the South Bank brings a modern urban flavour to the traditional country village fete. Hosted by the organisation 'home live art', which has a reputation for producing art works in unusual environments, the programme includes live art, performance art which you can participate in with three National Theatre actors, communal country dancing, plus loads of food and other produce.

2 Notting Hill Carnival

The Notting Hill Carnival is the UK's biggest street party. Featuring a parade of floats and a variety of styles of Caribbean music, dance and food, the carnival celebrates London's multicultural heritage. Join the party and dance the day and night away! It takes place in the Notting Hill district of West London over the August bank holiday weekend.

3 Batman Live

Part theatre, part circus act and part pure visual and special effects spectacle, this show is produced by 'Warner Bros Consumer Products', which should, I suppose, tell you that it's not going to be a serious piece of drama. In fact, it's really eye candy served up for all the family. Although the actors do their best, the storyline is not very strong. The emphasis is on the visual, especially the set pieces, including a fantastic giant Joker's head.

4 This is Design

The Design Museum has used various examples from its collection to make an exhibition which looks at the impact that modern design has on our daily lives. The collection includes classic designs like the Swiss army knife and the Mini car, as well as more mundane objects, such as road signs and utility clothing. Most of the designs aren't new, but it's still a fascinating exhibition which challenges the viewer to take a closer look at things around us that we usually take for granted.

5 The Floating Cinema

At first appearance, this event, put on by artists Nina Pope and Karen Guthrie as part of the Create11 summer festival, seems to be just a screen mounted on a boat. But there's more to it than that. Some films are projected onto the walls of buildings next to the canal where the boat is situated and one or two are followed by talks or workshops so that you can learn about the making of them in more depth. You don't have to be able to swim to attend, but you may get wet – the weather forecast for the weekend isn't great!

Reading out and about

2 Read the *What's on* guide on page 28 quickly. Find the following information.

1 Two events where you are a spectator rather than an active participant.

.....

.....

2 Two events which you can dance at.

.....

.....

3 Two events which you can eat at.

.....

.....

4 An event where you can work with actors.

.....

5 An event where you can hear an expert speak about their work.

.....

6 An event where different ethnic groups come together.

.....

7 An event that children and adults can enjoy.

.....

8 An event that you wouldn't normally find in a city.

.....

3 Find words in the guide for these definitions.

1 shared or enjoyed by everyone (para 1)

.....

2 a moving platform for performers (para 2)

.....

3 something good to look at, but without much usefulness (para 3)

.....

4 everyday, normal (para 4)

.....

5 seminar or discussion group led by an expert (para 5)

.....

Grammar expressions of quantity

4 Complete the sentences with expressions of quantity. Use one word in each space.

1 There will be a small ..... of actors at the Alternative Village Fete.

2 There is ..... carnival in the UK as big as Notting Hill.

3 There were ..... amazing set pieces in the *Batman Live* show.

4 There are ..... of different classic designs on show at the Design Museum.

5 Hardly ..... objects at the 'This is Design' exhibition will be new for the viewer.

6 A ..... films are accompanied by talks and workshops to discuss them in detail.

5 Choose the correct option to complete the sentences.

1 I really enjoyed the Alternative Village Fete – I even did *little / a little* dancing.

2 There aren't *much / enough* events like this in London.

3 There's *a lot of / much* international interest in the Notting Hill Carnival. *A large number of / A large amount of* the visitors this year were tourists.

4 I agree with the reviews – there were *plenty of / much* special effects in the Batman Live show, but there were *no / any* strong elements in the story.

5 We visited the website, but there was *a lack of / a little* clear information about the programme.

6 You don't see *several / many* new things at this exhibition, but you still learn a lot.

7 Book now, because when I phoned there were *hardly no / hardly any* tickets left.

8 There was *a bit of / a small number* of rain at the beginning, but it didn't spoil the show.

6 Pronunciation weak form *of*

1.31 Practise saying these sentences. Pay attention to the weak form of ***of***. Then listen and check.

1 First of all, just a few words of thanks.

2 Most of the time, it's a bit of a laugh.

3 As a matter of fact, he's a friend of mine.

4 That's kind of you, but it seems like a lot of trouble.

5 Of course it was just a bit of fun.

6 In spite of that, there were a number of volunteers.

4b Art or vandalism?

Vocabulary types of artwork

1 Label the pictures.

graffiti installation landscape portrait sculpture sketch still life

1 .....

2 .....

3 .....

4 .....

5 .....

6 .....

7 .....

Listening the graffiti debate

2 Look at the two photos of graffiti. Answer the questions.

1 Can you see any difference between them?

.....

2 Which do you find more attractive?

.....

3 1.32 Listen to a radio discussion programme about whether graffiti is vandalism or art. Answer the questions.

1 What event in the news prompted this discussion?

.....

.....

2 What is the graffiti artist Handy's view of this event?

.....

.....

3 When is graffiti vandalism according to Guy Francis?

.....

.....

4 1.32 Listen again and choose the correct option (a–c) to complete the statements.

1 In the second half of the programme, they will be discussing:
   a graffiti.
   b help at work.
   c unemployment.

2 Guy Francis is an expert on the subject because:
   a he used to be a graffiti artist himself.
   b he used to be a journalist who wrote about the arts.
   c he works for the *Daily News*, a graffiti magazine.

3 Handy thinks that whether graffiti is art or vandalism should not be decided by:
   a the gallery owners.
   b the public.
   c the courts.

4 According to Guy Francis, Tox's work was vandalism because:
   a it was very basic and poor art.
   b he broke into the property like a criminal.
   c the property owners didn't want graffiti on their property.

5 Tox's graffiti consisted of:
   a writing his name and the date.
   b writing imaginative images.
   c drawing his name in many different colours.

6 The graffiti artist Banksy's work:
   a is very popular.
   b is very cheap.
   c has upset many property owners.

Grammar determiners

5 Look at the first sentence in each pair. Then complete the second sentence so that it has the same meaning as the first.

1 I have notified all the people who were invited.
   I have notified every ..... .
2 I think that both methods work.
   I think that either ..... .
3 Almost no one came to the opening night.
   Hardly ..... .
4 We've spent every bit of our money.
   We've spent all ..... .
5 Each country has its own laws and rules.
   All ..... .
6 Everyone in the world is waiting to see what will happen.
   The whole ..... .

6 1.32 Complete the sentences from the radio discussion using these determiners. Then listen and check.

all any both each either every
no (x2) whole

1 Is ..... case different or are there measures we can take that will help ..... unemployed people get back to work?
2 There's ..... difference in this case.
3 Graffiti is either art or it's vandalism. You can't have it ..... ways.
4 If Tox had put his work in a gallery, there wouldn't have been ..... trouble.
5 ..... owner of that property complained.
6 All Tox does is to write his name over and over again. There are ..... imaginative images at all.
7 The ..... debate of whether it's art or not is a different matter.
8 ..... type of graffiti could be considered art.

7 Complete the passage. Choose the correct option.

There is [1] *no / any* way of telling what is art and what is not art any more. There is a story about a man who dropped his wallet in a modern art gallery. When he went back to get it, he found [2] *every / all the* visitors gathered around, admiring it. The message of the story is that [3] *the whole / all the* modern art world is a trick and [4] *each / either* viewer needs to be told whether something is art or not before they can admire it. But were the people wrong to admire the wallet? If they thought it was art, some people argue, then it was art. [5] *Both / either* views are possible. What's yours?

8 Dictation Banksy

1.33 Listen to a description of the work of the graffiti artist Banksy. Write down the words you hear. Then put the sentences in the correct order.

1 The message was clear: .....
   .....
2 Often it carries .....
   .....
3 Despite not .....
   .....
4 Banksy, who is .....
   .....
5 Banksy loves to .....
   .....

4c Music and me

Listening the importance of music

1 1.34 Listen to four people talking about what music means to them. Write down the type of music each one is talking about.

1 .....
2 .....
3 .....
4 .....

2 1.34 Read the sentences. Then listen again and match the speakers (1–4) with the correct sentences (a–f).

a Music is a way to escape from the boredom of your daily routine. .....
b Music can sum up what you are feeling. .....
c Music gives me a sense of belonging to a place. .....
d Music represents people's creative and independent side. .....
e Music is the most important part of our cultural identity. .....
f Music brings people together in celebration. .....

3 1.34 Listen again and complete the statements.

Speaker 1
1 ..... music tells stories about ..... life.

Speaker 2
2 In Brazil we have a big range of musical ..... to draw on.

Speaker 3
3 Millions of ..... have been able to express their feelings ... by listening to ..... music.

Speaker 4
4 People figured out how to make new ..... using old ..... .

4 Match these verbs with the phrases from the interviews.

be connected to (not) be important discover
escape seem true think of

1 It also **has to do with** our history .....
2 wanting to **break free** from the pressures of school .....
3 it **hit a chord** with us, for sure .....
4 people **figured out** how to make new sounds .....
5 they **came up with** something totally new .....
6 it **doesn't count for anything** .....

Word focus *cool*

5 Look at the sentences. Match the sentences (1–6) with the meanings of *cool* (a–d). Note the extra meaning (*OK/acceptable*).

a not warm
b stylish and fashionable
c calm
d OK/acceptable

1 Once you get past a certain age, you have no idea what's **cool** anymore.
2 I love September – bright sunny days and **cool** clear nights.
3 At school, I was the **coolest** person in the uncool group.
4 It's **cool** if you want to talk about it and it's **cool** if you don't.
5 It's not a good thing for a sportsperson to **lose their cool** in a moment of stress.
6 Her reaction to the idea of dancing was distinctly **cool**.

6 Match the beginnings of the sentences (1–4) with the endings (a–d).

1 Because he was 30 minutes late for the meeting,
2 I was worried that he would be angry, but
3 When he was young,
4 He's normally very calm, but on this occasion

a he was always trying to be cool.
b he said it was cool about it.
c he got a very cool reception.
d he lost his cool.

4d TV favourites

Real life describing likes and dislikes

1 1.35 Listen to a conversation in which Ian and Sue discuss a TV documentary. Answer the questions.

1 What was the documentary about?

.....

2 Why did Ian like it particularly?

.....

2 1.35 Listen again. Does Sue like (✓) or dislike (✗) the following.

1 nature documentaries in general ☐
2 the *Tribe* series ☐
3 people who make programmes about others living in difficult conditions ☐

3 1.35 Complete the phrases Ian and Sue use to express their likes and dislikes. Use up to four words in each space. Then listen again and check.

1 Oh, a nature documentary … not really my ..... actually.
2 I never ..... by them.
3 I'm ..... the presenter.
4 It ..... a bit actually.
5 I could ..... all day.
6 I guess I just get ..... people making these programmes.

4 Grammar extra word order with modifying adverbs

WORD ORDER WITH MODIFYING ADVERBS

- Adverbs that qualify adjectives come before the adjective.
  *I'm not **particularly** keen on reality TV shows.*
- Adverbs of intensity come before the main verb.
  *I **really** love musicals.*
- Never separate the main verb from its direct object.
  *I like **Bruce Parry** very much. (~~I like very much~~ ...)*

Look at the grammar box. Then put the words in the correct order.

1 listen / all day / I / Bach / can / to
.....
2 documentaries / anything / don't / for me / do / really
.....
3 into / really / I'm / TV / not
.....
4 particularly / on / keen / the presenter / not / I'm
.....
5 I / get / reality TV shows / of / a bit / tired
.....
6 TV / generally / watch / don't / much / I
.....

5 Pronunciation disappearing sounds

a 1.36 Listen to these words. Cross out the disappearing sound in each word.

1 documentary
2 everywhere
3 specifically
4 interest
5 separate
6 restaurant
7 listener
8 general

b 1.36 Practise saying each word. Then listen again and check.

6 Listen and respond describing likes and dislikes

1.37 Listen to the questions about your likes and dislikes. Respond with your own words. Then compare your response with the model answer that follows.

1 *What do you think of mobile phones with loud music ringtones?*

They really get on my nerves, especially when one starts ringing on the train or bus.

4e A comedy gig

1 Writing skill personalising your writing

Complete the features of personal and impersonal writing using these words.

active avoid contracted formal
furthermore I, we and you it passive
share uncontracted

Personal tone	Impersonal tone
a Use pronouns (e.g. .....)	Use pronouns (e.g. .....)
b Use ..... verbs	Use ..... verbs
c Use ..... forms (e.g. *isn't*)	Use ..... forms (e.g. *is not*)
d Use phrasal verbs	Use ..... verbs
e Add personal details	..... personal information
f Use conversational linking phrases (e.g. *what's more*)	Use formal linking phrases (e.g. .....)
g ..... your feelings	Be objective in your judgements

Writing an online review

2 Read the beginning of an online review for a comedy show. Underline examples of the features of personal writing (a–g) from Exercise 1. Label the features.

I've got to admit that I'm not a big fan of stand-up comedy. I always think that it's a rather unnatural thing. The comedian stands up in front of an audience who stare at him or her as if to say, 'Come on, then, make me laugh.' The comedian then has a few minutes to make them laugh or the audience will start to get restless. It's all a bit too aggressive and combative for me. So when I went with an old school friend to see new British comedian Spencer Brown last Tuesday night at the Bristol Comedy Club, I wasn't really looking forward to it.

3 Read the next paragraph of the review, which contains some features of impersonal writing. Rewrite the underlined words and expressions using personal forms.

[1] However, we quite enjoyed the show. And we [2] were not the only ones – [3] his act seemed to be liked by the rest of the audience too. Brown's technique is to [4] commence by telling a small joke – usually some amusing observation about daily life – which [5] it is imagined at first is the main joke. But [6] subsequently he builds on this by telling a joke [7] that is related to the first and then another. The effect of [8] combining jokes like this is that, even though each one may not be that funny by itself, the whole sequence is [9] in reality very funny.

1 .....
2 .....
3 .....
4 .....
5 .....
6 .....
7 .....
8 .....
9 .....

4 Complete the review by writing the last paragraph. Include a personal recommendation and details of when this show is on.

.....
.....
.....
.....
.....
.....
.....
.....
.....
.....

Wordbuilding suffixes

1 Choose the correct suffix for each word. Then write the words.

1 snow -scape / -ness / -ism .....
2 metalwork -ist / -ship / -er .....
3 craftsman -ism / -ship / -ness .....
4 polite -ness / -ist / -ship .....
5 saxophone -ship / -er / -ist .....
6 romantic -ness / -ism / -scape .....

2 Write the correct nouns using the correct suffixes.

1 the style of art that created surreal paintings .....
2 someone who plays the guitar .....
3 someone who presents a show on TV .....
4 a painting of a city view .....
5 the state of being calm .....
6 the arts movement that championed modern things .....
7 a picture showing the moon's surface .....
8 the ability to be a musician .....
9 someone who plays the trombone .....
10 someone who does carpentry .....
11 the quality of being direct .....
12 the state of being a companion .....

Learning skills asking about language

3 Sometimes to help you learn you will need to ask your teacher or a native speaker questions about the language. Look at the questions 1–6 and the answers a student has given.

1 Is 'mate' a slang expression for 'friend'? *Yes.*
2 Do you pronounce the 'g' in 'recognition'? *Yes.*
3 Why do you say 'rush hour' when the traffic isn't moving? *Everyone's rushing to get home.*
4 Is there a similar saying to 'to make two hits with one stone' in English? *Yes, 'to kill two birds with one stone'.*
5 Is 'You're welcome' an American or a British expression? *American, but the British use it too.*
6 Does 'I wonder if you can help me' sound too polite or is it OK? *It depends on the situation: it is very polite.*

4 Look at these words and phrases from the unit. Answer the questions.

1 Is 'cool' a slang expression? .....
2 How do you pronounce 'comfortable'? .....
3 Why do you say 'either way' but 'both ways'? .....
4 Is there a similar expression to 'it hits me on the nerves' in English? .....
5 Is 'hip-hop' an American or a British expression? .....
6 Does 'I can't bear ... something' sound too direct? .....

Check!

5 Do the quiz. All the answers are in Student's Book Unit 4.

1 COMPLETE THE QUOTES.

a 'Nature has done everything for Sydney, man nothing; man has done everything for ....., nature nothing.'

b '..... art is an imitation of nature.'

c 'Rap doesn't belong to ..... culture. It belongs here.'

2 WHAT ARE THESE WORDS BEGINNING WITH 'F'?

a the countable equivalent of 'little' .....

b traditional, local music .....

c a supporter or follower (especially of a sports team or pop group) .....

3 WHAT ARE THE OPPOSITES OF THESE THINGS?

a a personal tone .....

b a little bit of luck .....

c warm up .....

4 REARRANGE THE LETTERS TO MAKE WORDS.

a music: igg ..... siclry .....

b art: ketsch ..... luscerupt .....

c theatre: aply ..... lamicus .....

Unit 5 Development

5a Urban development

Listening rebuilding New Orleans

1 1.38 Listen to a local journalist describing the rebuilding work in New Orleans after Hurricane Katrina. Are the sentences true (T) or false (F)?

1 A lot of rebuilding work has taken place in the French Quarter.
2 More than half the residents who were evacuated from the city have returned.
3 One project is helping to build affordable homes.
4 The new homes are very simple, practical houses.

Glossary
levee (n) /ˈlevi/ a barrier to protect an area from flooding
spare (v) /speə/ save from something

2 1.38 Listen to the journalist again and complete the sentences.

1 For most tourists who visit New Orleans these days, things seem to be .....
2 Most of the damage in New Orleans was caused by the ....., not the .....
3 Most New Orleanians ..... their city.
4 The redevelopment plan for New Orleans has not been systematic or .....
5 The Lower 9th Ward was a pretty ..... area of New Orleans, even before the storm.
6 The new homes are ..... and environmentally-friendly.
7 The journalist thought the designs of the buildings were very .....
8 Some critics say that the houses are not .....

Grammar verb + infinitive or *-ing*

3 Look at the sentences from the report about the rebuilding work in New Orleans. Choose the correct option.

1 In the French Quarter, everything now seems *being / to be* back to normal.
2 In other areas, you keep on *seeing / to see* the effects of the disaster.
3 The city's levees failed *holding / to hold* the big tidal wave back.
4 About two-thirds of the residents have managed *returning / to return*.
5 A few people decided *resettling / to resettle* elsewhere.
6 One project proposed *building / to build* 150 affordable homes.
7 No one wants to risk *seeing / to see* their home flood again.
8 You can't help *wondering / to wonder* how many more homes could have been built.

4 Complete the table with these verbs. Some verbs can go in more than one category.

allow ask carry on enjoy get
help hope imagine make want

verb + *to* + infinitive (1)	verb + *someone* + *to* + infinitive (2)
.....	.....
.....	.....
.....	.....
.....	.....
.....	.....
verb + *-ing* (3)	**verb + *someone* + infinitive** (4)
.....	.....
.....	.....
.....	.....
.....	.....
.....	.....
.....	.....

5 Grammar extra verb + infinitive or *-ing*

a Put these verbs into the correct column in the table in Exercise 4 on page 36.

avoid 3 choose 1 finish 3 force 2 involve 3
learn 1 let 4 (not) mind 3 teach 2

b Complete the text about volunteering in New Orleans using the correct form of the verb in brackets.

If you want [1] to (visit) New Orleans as a tourist, but would also like to do something to help local people [2] rebuild (rebuild) their lives while you are there, you could work as a volunteer on a project. There are lots of organisations that allow visitors [3] to (participate) for a week or even a few days. If you don't mind [4] getting (get) your hands dirty, you could do some labouring on a building project. Alternatively, you could choose [5] to (work) with children or help out at a local museum. Some of the projects might involve [6] learning (learn) a few new skills, but no one will force you [7] to (do) something you feel uncomfortable with. And don't worry about not having fun. You will have plenty of time off and you'll also enjoy [8] meeting (meet) New Orleanians – something a regular tourist might find more difficult.

Vocabulary urban development

6 Complete the announcement by a city's Planning Committee. Use these words.

centre district housing luxury
mall pedestrianised spaces waterfront

On 2nd July, the City Council's Planning Committee met and agreed the following actions to **transform** the city:

- The centre should become a [1] ..... zone to allow shoppers and visitors to walk around more freely.
- The old shopping [2] ..... in Prince's Street, next to the river, will be **demolished**. The council will invite designs for a new [3] ..... development in its place. It wants the area to be **redeveloped** as a mixed residential area: some [4] ..... apartments and some affordable [5] .....
- It was also agreed that a lack of green [6] ..... **spoils** the appearance of the centre. The plan is to encourage companies to move to a new business [7] ..... in the north of the city and **convert** existing car parks into garden areas.
- The council also proposes to **modernise** the new leisure [8] ..... in the north of the city.

7 Match the verbs in bold in Exercise 6 with these verbs.

1 bring up to date .....
2 change completely .....
3 damages .....
4 knocked down .....
5 rebuilt .....
4 turn .....

8 Dictation a New Orleanian speaks

a 1.39 Listen to a New Orleans resident describing life since Hurricane Katrina. Write down the words you hear. Is the resident happy living in New Orleans?

The fact that .....

.....

.....

.....

.....

I'm a musician .....

.....

.....

.....

.....

But since Hurricane Katrina, ...

.....

.....

.....

.....

b Underline examples of verb + infinitive or verb + *-ing* in your answer in Exercise 8a.

5b Monterey Bay

Reading Changing places

1 Read the article about Monterey Bay. Which of the following sentences are true of Monterey today?

a It has an important tourist industry.
b It is a cosmopolitan place.
c It has an important fishing industry.
d There is little sea-life left.

2 Read the article again. Are the sentences true (T) or false (F). Or is there not enough information (N) to say if the statements are true or false?

1 In the last 150 years, Monterey's main industry has been tourism, then fishing, then tourism again.
2 Canning was a process that was invented in Monterey.
3 Carl Danielsen was born in Norway.
4 A lot of immigrants came to Monterey to take advantage of the boom in fishing.
5 The reason for the disappearance of the sardines is unclear.
6 Otters like to eat abalone.
7 It's impossible to make a living from fishing in Monterey these days.
8 The essential character of Monterey hasn't changed because its industry still centres around the sea and sea-life.

3 Find words or phrases in the passage with the following definitions.

1 in the meantime (para 1)
.....
2 be part of the good times (para 2)
.....
3 suddenly (para 3)
.....
4 senior and experienced people (para 3)
.....
5 establish, start (para 3)
.....
6 try out (para 4)
.....

Glossary
abalone (n) /æbə'ləʊni/ a small edible shellfish
canning process (n) /'kænɪŋ 'prəʊses/ preserving food by putting it in a tin
otter (n) /'ɒtə(r)/ a small river or sea animal

The history and development of Monterey Bay is a dynamic one. 150 years ago tourism was its main industry, as it is again today. But a lot of changes have taken place in the intervening period. Carl Danielsen, a fisherman in Monterey for the last 60 years, describes these changes.

'My father was a fisherman and his father before him. I first started going out to sea with my daddy when I was seven years old. In those days, there were a lot of sardines in the sea and Monterey took advantage of the newly-developed canning process, which meant that enormous amounts of fish could be preserved in a way that wasn't possible before. In the 1930s, Monterey was the world capital of the sardine canning industry and fishing was big business here. That was when my parents came over from Norway, along with other immigrants from Japan, China, Italy – you name it. Everyone wanted to join in the party. That's one of the reasons that Monterey is such a cosmopolitan place now.

Then in the 1950s, the sardines disappeared – just like that. No one knows why. Some people say it was because of overfishing; others say it was just part of the natural ocean cycle. One thing is for sure, and that is that fishing isn't the simple industry it was in the 1950s – I wish it was. There have been so many rules and regulations since then, controlling what and where you can fish. You can't collect abalone, for example, anymore – unless you're an otter, that is! Old-timers like me continue to fish, but it's not an easy life and many people have set up other businesses. Most are tourist-related, like boat trips, sightseeing trips and fishing trips, but all of them are connected with the sea and sea-life. We have a fantastic range of sea-life here: otters, whales, dolphins, and so on.

So today, tourism is the main industry here, but the essential character of the bay hasn't changed. The old canning factory has become an aquarium and a research centre for sea-life. There are lots of restaurants along the sea front, which do great business. I'd recommend any visitor to Monterey to sample the seafood. It's fantastic.'

4 Complete the sentences with the correct adjective. Use the nouns in brackets to help you.

1 Monterey is a ..... place. (dynamism)
2 In the 1930s, Monterey was a more ..... city. (industry)
3 Now it has become an ..... destination for tourists. (attraction)
4 The old harbour is well ..... . (preservation)
5 These days, fishing is strongly ..... . (regulation)
6 But the ..... character of the bay hasn't changed. (essence)

Grammar verbs with *-ing* and *to* + infinitive

5 Read the pairs of sentences. Do the verbs have a change in their meaning (C) or no change in meaning (NC)?

1 a When did they **start** to can sardines in Monterey?
b When did they **start** canning sardines in Monterey? ____

2 a People **continued** to can sardines in Monterey until the 1980s.
b People **continued** canning sardines in Monterey until the 1980s. ____

3 a I **stopped** to visit my aunt in California last year.
b I **stopped** visiting my aunt in California last year. ____

4 a Did you **remember** to bring a guidebook?
b Did you **remember** bringing a guidebook? ____

5 a I **like** to watch sea-life in the wild.
b I **like** watching sea-life in the wild. ____

6 a I **prefer** to eat fresh fish to frozen.
b I **prefer** eating fresh fish to frozen. ____

7 a He **went on** to work as a fisherman.
b He **went on** working as a fisherman. ____

8 a Every fisherman **means** to get up early in the morning.
b Being a fisherman **means** getting up early each morning. ____

6 Complete the sentences using the *-ing* form or *to* + infinitive.

1 Carl remembers ..... (go) fishing with his father in the 1950s.
2 In those days, preserving fish meant ..... (put) them into cans.
3 In the 1950s, fishermen had to stop ..... (catch) sardines.
4 Carl regrets ..... (say) that fishing is not a simple industry anymore.
5 Some older fishermen have gone on ..... (fish) to this day.
6 They try ..... (make) a living from it, but it's not an easy way of life.
7 Other fishermen stopped fishing ..... (go) into the tourist business.
8 Visitors to Monterey should try ..... (eat) the fresh seafood.

7 Choose the correct option to complete the text.

A lot of people visit Monterey Bay before going on [1] *visiting / to visit* San Francisco and Yellowstone Park in northern California. One thing they stop [2] *seeing / to see* are the otters which live in the harbour. While eating your lunch at a waterfront restaurant, you can watch them playing in the water or trying [3] *opening / to open* shellfish by breaking them against the fishing boats. Although the otters don't mean [4] *doing / to do* any harm, it annoys the fishermen because it means [5] *having / to have* to paint their boats more often!

8 **Pronunciation rhyming words**

1.40 Make pairs of rhyming words. Match the words in box A with the word that rhymes from box B. Then listen and check.

A China found front meant ocean placed rule way whale where

B drowned hunt minor motion sent share taste they'll tool weigh

5c Sustainable development?

Listening eco-cities

1 1.41 Read the sentences about eco-cities in China. Then listen to the interview with an architect. Are the sentences true (T) or false (F)?

1 China is a focus for eco-cities because it has so many new cities.
2 If you have the support of politicians, building an eco-city is relatively simple.
3 Construction workers already have the skills needed to build eco-cities.
4 Electric vehicles are favoured in eco-cities.
5 An eco-city must import as little energy, food and water from outside as possible.

Glossary
pipe dream (n) /ˈpaɪp driːm/ a fantasy that will never become reality
political will (n) /pəˈlɪtɪk(ə)l wɪl/ the support of politicians
skyway (n) /ˈskʌɪweɪ/ a road in the air
UV light (n) /ˈjuːviː laɪt/ ultra-violet light

2 1.41 Listen to the interview again and complete the facts.

1 Number of Chinese cities of one million-plus inhabitants by 2025: ..... .
2 In an eco-city there can be no ..... .
3 Chinese saying: 'Anything is ....., but nothing is ..... .'
4 People who need to coordinate efforts: planners, architects, ... firms and local ..... interests.
5 Another important consideration is the ..... that go into the building.
6 The layout should encourage people to ..... to work.
7 Transportation must be ..... .
8 No energy should be ..... .
9 Rain water is collected and made safe using ..... light.
10 Vegetables are grown in large ..... .

Word focus *pick*

3 Look at the phrases with the word *pick*. Choose the correct definition.

1 There's no shortage of good designs and clever ideas out there – you can **take your pick**.
a relax b choose from many
c study them in your own time

2 Can I just **pick up on** something we mentioned earlier, which is the question on waste?
a question b highlight c return to

3 The other difficulty is **picking your way through** all the bureaucracy and regulations.
a examining b being very careful with
c finding a route through

4 Complete the sentences using the appropriate phrase with *pick* from the list below.

take your pick pick holes in pick on
pick up (x2) pick your brains

1 I don't know why you always ..... me to do these boring administrative jobs!
2 The restaurant has been very quiet, but business will ..... in the spring.
3 Can you ..... me ..... from the train station at 5.30?
4 I don't mind which desk you sit at – ..... .
5 There are always people who will try to ..... a new eco-solution or idea and tell you why it isn't ecological.
6 Can I ..... about a venue for my parents' 25th wedding anniversary?

5 Pronunciation antepenultimate stress

a 1.42 Often in words of three or more syllables, the stress falls on the third syllable from the end. Listen to the stress in these words and repeat.

photograph photographer analyse
analysis analytical

b 1.43 Underline the stressed syllable in these words. Then listen, check and repeat.

architect architectural electricity
energy generate material minimise
political sustainable sustainability

5d A development project

Real life reaching decisions

1 Match phrases (1–6) from list A with phrases with a similar meaning from list B (a–f).

A	B
1 I find it … that	a That's absolutely right.
2 If you ask me, …	b Not necessarily.
3 Is everyone OK with that?	c I agree.
4 I'd go along with that.	d That seems … to me.
5 Let's not …	e The way I see it, …
6 Exactly.	f Are we all agreed?
7 That depends.	g We shouldn't …

2 Look at these phrases about urban features. Write the opposites.

1 private transport
p..... transport

2 luxury housing
a..... housing

3 out-of-town shops
l..... shops

4 built-up areas
g..... spaces

5 streets where cars can drive
p..... zones

6 places where people work
l..... facilities

3 1.44 Listen to four conversations about reaching decisions. Who is speaking in each conversation? Write the correct letter (a–d).

Conversation 1	a bankers
Conversation 2	b councillors
Conversation 3	c neighbours
Conversation 4	d friends

4 1.44 Listen again and circle the phrase you hear.

Conversation 1
Colin: *I find it incredible that / It seems incredible to me that* in a big city like this there aren't more leisure facilities. We've got one rather ancient swimming pool, a few tennis courts and a few children's playgrounds.

Jen: *I see your point. / I know what you mean.* I think we should get together and write a petition to the local council asking them to do something about it.

Conversation 2
Michelle: The problem is that no developer has any incentive to build affordable housing. They all make far more money from luxury homes. *If you ask me, / Personally,* I think it's a disgrace. *What's your view? / What do you think?*

Ruth: Well, *I agree, / I'd go along with that,* but I'm just not sure there's much that we, as a council, can do about it. *We ought to have / We probably need* to consider a completely different solution to the housing problem.

Conversation 3
Liz: So, the GFC is asking for a further loan to develop their food co-operative project. *What do you think we should do? / What's your view?*

Steve: *If you ask me, / The way I see it,* they have done a good job so far and made all their repayments on time. But *it's really a question of / it really depends on* what they need the money for.

John: *Exactly. / That's absolutely right.* So, we'll ask them to submit a more detailed proposal. *Is everyone OK with that? / Are we all agreed on that?*

Conversation 4
Alex: Have you seen the plans for that new house across the street? It looks awful: not at all like the other houses round here. *Personally, I think / If you ask me,* we should oppose it.

Nick: Well, *we shouldn't be / let's not be* too hasty. I think it would be better to talk to the new owners first about it. We want to try to keep on good terms with them.

5 Listen and respond reaching decisions

1.45 Listen to five people expressing their views. Respond with your own words. Then compare your response with the model answer that follows.

1

What do you think of that new shopping mall they are building in the centre of town?

Personally, I think it's horrible. I'd prefer to see more local shops.

5e Urban sprawl

Writing an opinion essay

1 Read the paragraphs from an opinion essay on the topic 'Is urban sprawl a good thing?' Put the paragraphs in the correct order.

1 ..... 2 ..... 3 ..... 4 .....

A

In the heart of the city, on the other hand, life for residents is tougher. They have no garden, there is more pollution, and probably also more crime and poverty. In addition, rents are high. Because of this, more and more people aspire to live in the suburbs and the city keeps spreading.

B

In 1965, two futurists predicted, 'By the year 2000, the area in the north-eastern United States between Boston and Washington DC, a distance of 450 miles, will form one big megalopolis.' They were wrong, but not far wrong! Towns and cities continue to grow outwards. As a result, the space they occupy grows bigger and the rural areas around them grow smaller. This is known as 'urban sprawl'. It seems to be a natural phenomenon, but is it a good one and should it be stopped?

C

There is nothing wrong with wanting to have the best of both town and country, but unless planners do something to reverse this trend, our city centres will become dark and dangerous places and eventually they will die. The only answer is to limit urban sprawl and refocus our efforts on making our city centres more pleasant places to live.

D

Urban sprawl takes place because people want to have the benefits of both city and country. In suburbia, they can have a nice home, a piece of land, a peaceful and safe environment, and convenient transport links into the city where, in all probability, they work.

2 Which of the following techniques does the writer use to begin the essay?

a giving a dramatic example of the problem (perhaps from your own experience)
b giving some statistics that illustrate the seriousness of the problem
c quoting what someone (often famous) has said about this problem

3 Rewrite the opening sentence(s) to this essay using one of the other techniques.

4 Find expressions in the essay that mean the same as the following.

1 As well as this (para A) .....
2 Consequently (para A and B)
.....
.....
3 in contrast (para A) .....

5 Writing skill linking words

a Look at the examples (a–d). Notice that the linking phrases need to be followed by a noun or the *-ing* form of the verb.

a **In addition to** this, cities are becoming more polluted.
b **As well as** this growth outwards, there is also more congestion in cities
c **Because of** growing outwards, cities are taking up valuable green space.
d **As a result of** cities growing outwards, we are losing valuable green space.

b Rewrite the sentences using the linking phrases given.

1 The house comes with three acres of land and a swimming pool.
As well as .....
2 People have moved out of the centre because crime has risen.
As a result of .....
3 We have a good bus service and excellent roads into the city centre.
In addition to .....
4 We are starting to redevelop city centres because there are restrictions on building on green spaces.
Because of .....

Wordbuilding adverb + adjective

1 Complete the sentences with these adverb + adjective phrases.

cleverly designed economically disadvantaged
ethnically mixed highly cultured ill prepared
long-term unemployed politically correct
upwardly mobile

1 It is very difficult for ..... people to get back into work, because they lose confidence.
2 These days you have to be ..... in your use of language so that you don't discriminate between people of different sex or race.
3 Nowadays, we say someone is ..... instead of 'poor'.
4 They are an ..... family: her father was a miner; her daughter is now a top criminal lawyer.
5 I was ..... for the meeting. Everyone else had read all the background information.
6 London is a very ..... city. You can find people from most parts of the world living there.
7 It's a ..... society in which it is common for ordinary people to visit museums and go to the theatre.
8 The houses, although small, are ..... with a lot of space inside.

Wordbuilding prefix *re-* with verbs and nouns

2 Complete the sentences using an appropriate verb with the prefix *re-*. Use the root words below to help you

adjust build decorate do read train

1 They are trying to ..... their lives after the floods.
2 I think we need to ..... this room – the walls are a depressing colour
3 He has left his job in banking and plans to ..... as a teacher.
4 When you return home after a long stay abroad, it takes time to ..... .
5 If your homework has too many mistakes in it, the teacher will ask you to ..... it.
6 It's such a great book. I've ..... it four times!

Learning skills critical thinking when you read

3 It is useful to apply critical thinking techniques when you read a text. Read these steps:

- Always scan the text quickly to get a general idea of the topic before you read it in detail.
- Look at who wrote it and for whom. Think about why they wrote the text.
- Read it carefully and note down the main points.
- Does the author develop a particular theme or argument? Is this presented logically?
- Do you agree or disagree with the argument?
- What other knowledge about the subject do you have? Does it fit with the arguments in the article?
- If you are interested in the topic, follow up your reading by researching more about the subject.

4 Look back at the article on page 58 of the Student's Book. Use the critical thinking techniques above and write your answers.

Check!

5 Do the quiz. You can find the answers in Student's Book Unit 5.

Quiz

1 Which of these does NOT describe a type of development?
a personal
b sustainable
c life

2 Which of these is NOT in Dubai?
a the world's tallest building
b the world's biggest shopping mall
c the world's busiest airport

3 Kerala is a happy society because the government has invested a lot in ... .
a agriculture
b political involvement
c health and education

4 Who were the main critics of the Nam Theun 2 hydro-power project?
a the local villagers
b environmentalists
c the World Bank

5 Which of these phrases has the same meaning as *In addition*?
a Then again
b Furthermore
c Consequently

Unit 6 Alternative travel

6a Staycations

Listening personal experiences

1 2.1 Listen to four people talking about their idea of a staycation. Write the number of the speaker next to what's most important for them in a staycation. There are two extra items.

a planning your staycation ☐
b going back to a simpler way of life ☐
c changing your routine ☐
d getting help at home ☐
e spoiling yourself ☐
f filling the days with stimulating new experiences ☐

2 2.1 Listen again and put the number of the speaker next to the activity they suggest. There are two extra activities.

a spending family time just chatting and playing ☐
b taking your children on day trips ☐
c learning a new sport ☐
d enjoying the experience of shopping for food ☐
e eating out often ☐
f getting a little exercise each day ☐

3 Look at the phrases in bold from the listening. Choose the correct definition.

1 By staying at home, you're not necessarily going to **switch off**.
   a forget about work
   b feel out of touch with the world
   c get more rest

2 I'm not trying to **be prescriptive**, but you must make some rules.
   a frighten you
   b tell you exactly what to do
   c be funny

3 My idea of a staycation is to **pamper myself**.
   a go to the health club
   b spoil myself
   c do healthy things

4 I organised things to do every day. Maybe my family thought I **overdid** it.
   a wanted to impress people
   b organised too much
   c spent a lot of money

5 Modern life shouldn't **dictate** your routine.
   a interfere with
   b destroy
   c control

Grammar *not*

4 Rewrite the phrases in bold in the negative form.

1 **Let's kid ourselves** that just by staying at home, you're going to relax.

.....

2 **Answer** the phone – switch on the answer phone.

.....

3 **You have to do** a big weekly shop, for example.

.....

4 It would be easier **to do** things to keep fit.

.....

5 **I think it's extravagant**, because I know I'm spending less than I would on holiday.

.....

6 I hope **I overdid it**.

.....

7 I tried **to let the children know** I was worried.

.....

8 So **you really must let** modern life dictate what you do too much.

.....

5 Rewrite the sentences using negative forms and the words given.

1 I won't have a coffee now, thanks.
..... WANT

2 It doesn't seem to me to be a great idea.
..... THINK

3 We shouldn't do anything to upset them.
..... LET

4 I'm worried that I gave her the wrong impression.
..... HOPE

5 You can give the book back to me when you like.
.....
..... HAVE/IMMEDIATELY

6 Don't be late, please.
..... TRY

7 It is forbidden to take food into the library.
..... MUST

8 Have they decided to leave?
..... STAY

Vocabulary travel

6 Complete the description of a holiday. Write one word in each space.

We had a great holiday, thanks. Up until September, I had only had two days [1] ..... all year. We booked a self-[2] ..... apartment in a little village in Pelion in the north of Greece. Pelion has lovely [3] ..... : wooded hills leading down to beautiful little coves and a crystal clear sea. Our apartment was in a village a little way up in the hills with a fantastic [4] ..... of the sea. We flew with one of the low-budget [5] ..... – I think our return flights were less than £100 each. We only took hand [6] ..... with us because on low-budget flights they charge extra for each bag you take. Then we rented a car to get us from the airport to our accommodation. It was quite a long [7] ..... but we went through very pretty [8] ..... . Coming back was expensive, though. The drive to the airport [9] ..... about three hours longer because of roadworks. So the car hire company charged us for an extra half day. Then the airline said my [10] ..... was too big and it would have to go in the hold – for an extra £80! I couldn't believe it.

Vocabulary phrasal verbs with *in* and *out*

7 Complete the sentences using the correct verb.

1 Shall we ..... in tonight and see what's on the TV? I'm too tired to go out.

2 Please ..... in and see us anytime. You're always welcome.

3 I don't like ..... out. I'd much rather just cook a meal at home.

4 Don't ..... out too late. You've got an interview in the morning.

5 You wouldn't believe the bureaucracy. We had to ..... in about ten forms!

6 The party starts at 8 p.m. Please bring a friend and come and ..... in the fun!

8 Dictation staycations

2.2 Listen to a travel expert describing the trend in staycations. He makes four points. Write the words that you hear. Do you agree with him?

1 In tough economic times, ...
.....
.....

2 However, they .....
.....
.....

3 You don't have to .....
.....
.....

4 I don't think .....
.....
.....

6b Why volunteer?

Why volunteer?

Volunteering is one of the most rewarding ways you can make a real difference to people who live in very tough circumstances. Most people join us because they want to give something back and find they get much more in return.

VSO sends volunteers rather than money. We work on long-term, sustainable solutions. And volunteers are how we do it. Nothing compares with the satisfaction of translating generosity into practical, life-changing achievements.

Our short-term roles give experienced professionals the opportunity to make a concentrated, high-impact contribution to the fight against poverty. You'll face fresh challenges, develop valuable new skills, and experience another culture in a way few people have the opportunity to.

Who can be a short-term volunteer?

Our placements tend to be consultancy-type roles, which are designed to achieve a specific goal or complete a set project, so they require highly skilled professionals who can hit the ground running. The majority of short-term roles last between four and six months.

For most of our roles, you will need at least five years' experience in your field of work, be able to stay for six months, and be ready to leave within eighteen months of applying – sometimes at short notice. VSO matches volunteers to placements where they are most professionally suited. It helps if you're flexible when considering where you're willing to work.

How we'll support you

This isn't 'voluntourism' – you don't have to pay to volunteer with VSO. We take care of all your expenses, from flights and insurance through to visas and accommodation. You even get a local living allowance. For more information, see our volunteering FAQs.

The skills we're looking for

We are currently looking for short-term volunteers in the following sectors: advocacy specialists, agricultural specialists, business and management specialists, financial specialists, fundraisers, IT specialists, monitoring and evaluation specialists, researchers, other specialist and one-off roles.

If you don't yet have the level of experience to undertake a short-term role, you can look at the long-term opportunities in your area of work.

Reading VSO

1 Read the information from the VSO website. Complete the notes about the short-term voluntary roles.

Type of work: [1] .....

Skills and experience required: [2] .....

Length of stay: [3] .....

Flexibility on dates: [4] .....

Costs: [5] .....

2 Read the information again and choose the correct option (a–c).

1 People who *want to give something back* means people who want to … .
   a repay VSO for giving them a job
   b give money to the organisation
   c make a contribution to society

2 Short-term volunteer jobs are open to people … .
   a who like project work
   b with some work expertise
   c who have already worked as consultants

3 *Hit the ground running* (paragraph 3) means … .
   a start work immediately
   b be very adaptable
   c use your intelligence

4 When placing people, VSO especially takes into account a volunteer's … .
   a wishes
   b willingness to work
   c work background

5 Which of the following volunteer costs does VSO NOT pay for?
   a travel
   b day-to-day expenses
   c hotel bills

6 The article suggests that long-term posts could be suitable for people who are … .
   a less experienced travellers
   b less advanced in their careers
   c less confident

3 Read the information again and find adjectives that mean:

1 satisfying (para 1) .....
2 very difficult (para 1) .....
3 intensive (para 3) .....
4 new (para 3) .....
5 fixed (para 4) .....
6 not to be repeated (para 7) .....

Grammar negative and tag questions

4 Complete these negative questions for people who are thinking of becoming volunteers.

1 *Haven't you ever wondered* (you / ever / wonder) what it would be like to be a volunteer in another country rather than just a tourist?
2 You clearly care about others. Why ..... (you / translate) your concerns into concrete action?
3 ..... (you / would like) to use your skills to help others?
4 ..... (it / harm) your future career to take time away from work?
5 ..... (you / going to lose out) financially if you become a volunteer for nine months?
6 ..... (it / be) selfish to want to do this for your own personal development?

5 Look at the questions that a potential VSO volunteer asks. Complete them with question tags.

1 A: You don't organise two-week volunteer vacations, ... ?
   B: No, we don't.
2 A: But the work would be suitable for a gap-year student, ... ?
   B: Well, no. It's aimed at an older age group.
3 A: It isn't suitable for my 18-year-old daughter, then, ... ?
   B: No, I'm afraid it isn't.
4 A: But you used to take younger volunteers, ... ?
   B: Yes, but our policy has changed.
5 A: So, as a teacher, there might be possibilities for me to volunteer, ... ?
   B: Absolutely, for a longer-term post.
6 A: And I'd have to be flexible about where and when I could go, ... ?
   B: Well, of course, flexibility helps.

6 Pronunciation intonation in questions

2.3 Look at the questions. Does the intonation rise (R) or fall (F) at the end? Then listen and check.

	R	F
1 It's a fantastic idea, isn't it?	☐	☐
2 Wouldn't it be great if everyone did this?	☐	☐
3 Have you heard of VSO?	☐	☐
4 You can't really make that kind of long-term commitment, can you?	☐	☐
5 Didn't you do some volunteering when you were a student?	☐	☐
6 I don't have the right qualifications, do I?	☐	☐
7 Do you know any other organisations like VSO?	☐	☐
8 It would be interesting to talk to someone who's done it, wouldn't it?	☐	☐

6c Unusual trips

Listening a cruise with a difference

1 2.4 You are going to listen to a review of a cruise. Look at these words. Tick (✓) the items you would expect to find on a cruise ship. Then listen and compare which items are on the *NG Endeavour*.

a crane	☐	a microscope	☐
a kayak	☐	an inflatable rubber boat	☐
a casino	☐	restaurants	☐
shops	☐	guides	☐

2 2.4 Listen again. How does the review describe *NG Endeavour* cruises? Choose the correct the option.

1 entertaining / educational
2 reasonable / expensive
3 comfortable / uncomfortable
4 well-equipped / basic
5 exciting / monotonous

3 2.4 Complete the table with information about the *NG Endeavour*. Then listen again and complete any missing details.

Name of ship	*NG Endeavour*
Type of ship	Cruise ship converted from a [1] ..... trawler.
Fares	From [2] ..... to [3] ..... a day
Special gadgets	[4] ..... [5] ....., Zodiacs
On-board staff	[6] ..... and expert [7] .....
Places it visits	Svalbard in the Arctic circle, the [8] ..... and [9] .....
Eating facilities	one [10] ..... room

4 Look at the transcript on page page 120–121 and find words or expressions that mean:

1 spending time lazily and luxuriously (para 1) .....
2 fixed in a way that cannot be changed (para 2) .....
3 a good amount of (para 3) .....
4 rich (para 4) .....
5 easy to talk to (para 5) .....
6 during the whole (para 6) .....

Word focus *mind*

5 Rewrite the sentences using expressions with *mind*.

1 **If you were thinking of a cruise**, try one of Lindblad's expeditions.
..... (have in mind)
2 **If a bit of danger and excitement are not a problem for you**, Lindblad cruises are perfect.
..... (don't mind)
3 The cruises are amazing. **Admittedly**, they're not cheap.
..... (mind you)
4 **Remember that** these are not typical cruises.
..... (bear in mind)
5 I used to think that cruises were for the old and retired, **but I've got a different opinion** now.
..... (change one's mind)
6 **I want to go** on one of their cruises, **but it's quite expensive**.
..... (be in two minds)

6 Grammar extra negative expressions

a Look at these negative expressions.

a **Don't** judge a book by its cover.
b **No** problem.
c It **doesn't** matter.

b Complete these common expressions using the correct negative forms.

1 ..... worry.
2 ..... worries.
3 ..... make sense.
4 ..... way!
5 ..... say a word.
6 ..... work like that.

6d Navigation

Real life getting around

1 2.5 Complete the sentences using prepositions. Then listen to a conversation between two friends and check.

1 I'll be coming ..... on the five o'clock train.
2 I can't pick you ....., I'm afraid.
3 How do I get ..... Sara's Café?
4 Just hop ..... any bus from the station.
5 Look ..... for the pier and get off there.
6 You'll see the café ..... your right.
7 If I get held ....., I'll call you.
8 I'll come ..... and meet you.

2 2.5 Listen again and answer the questions.

1 Why can't Steve meet Joe at the station?

.....

.....

2 How will Joe get to the meeting point?

.....

.....

3 Where do they arrange to meet in the end?

.....

.....

3 Rewrite the sentences so that they have the same meaning. Use the words in brackets.

1 The easiest option is to take the bus.
..... (thing)
2 Another possibility is to take a taxi.
..... (alternatively)
3 I can get there on my own.
..... (way)
4 It only takes fifteen minutes by bus.
..... (ride)
5 I'm arriving by train.
..... (coming)
6 If I am delayed, I'll let you know.
..... (held)

4 Choose the correct word to complete the situations.

crossing drive flight ride (x2) walk

1 It's a twenty-minute ..... . (car)
2 It's a two-hour ..... . (plane)
3 It's a fifteen-minute ..... . (bus)
4 It's a twenty-minute ..... . (foot)
5 It's a ten-minute ..... . (taxi)
6 It's a one-hour ..... . (ferry boat)

5 **Pronunciation intonation in sentences with two clauses**

a 2.6 Match the sentence halves. Then listen and check.

1 I'd prefer to drive,
2 It's not difficult to find,
3 I could come and meet you,
4 The bus is cheap,
5 You could take a taxi,

a but I don't finish work until 6.00 p.m.
b but it's quite a long way from the station.
c but it's a very scenic walk.
d but the car is behaving strangely.
e but it makes a lot of stops on the way.

b 2.6 Practise saying the sentences using the correct intonation.

6 **Listen and respond getting around**

2.7 Listen to a friend asking you for directions to your house from the town centre. Respond with your own words. Then compare your response with the model answer that follows.

1 *Hi there. I'm coming in on the train tomorrow at two o'clock. What's the best way to get to your house from there?*

The easiest thing is to take the bus.

6e Unfair charges

Writing a letter of complaint

1 Read the letter of complaint and answer the questions.

1 What is the woman's complaint?

.....

.....

2 What action does she want to be taken?

.....

.....

24 Clifford Gardens
Oxford
OX3 2FG

U-Fly Airlines
108 Pembroke Road
London
W8 7NP

Dear Sir/Madam

I am writing to register a complaint about having to pay extra charges to your airline on a recent flight to Spain (UZ485 from London to Seville on 3rd May). I feel that these charges were unjust.

At the time that I booked this flight, I read the terms about luggage carefully. The terms clearly stated that each passenger's hand luggage allowance was one bag measuring no more than 56 x 45 x 25cm and weighing up to 10 kilograms.

On arrival at check-in, I informed the member of the ground crew that my bag met these regulations, but she insisted that the coat that I was wearing should be placed in the bag. I attempted to pack the coat into my bag, but it would not fit, so I was instructed that I would have to pay £30 if I wished to take it onto the plane.

I was concerned that I was delaying other passengers, and consequently I opted to pay the money. Otherwise, I would certainly have disputed the charge, as I am now doing. It is perfectly reasonable to wear a coat onto a plane.

Given these circumstances, I would ask you firstly to refund the £30 to me and secondly to investigate the matter so that you can ensure that other passengers do not encounter the same problem.

Yours faithfully
Amelia Doyle

2 Answer these questions.

1 Where is the writer writing from?

.....

2 What is her relationship to the recipient of the letter? .....

3 What is the tone of the letter (e.g. formal/semi-formal)? .....

3 Writing skill formal language

a Find formal phrases in the letter with the same meaning as these less formal words.

1 complain .....
2 unfair .....
3 said .....
4 told .....
5 put .....
6 tried .....
7 wanted .....
8 chose .....
9 the situation .....
10 look into .....

b Rewrite the first paragraph of this letter of complaint using more formal language. Use these verbs to help you. You can change other words too.

consist give register regret serve state suffer

Dear Sir/Madam

I'm writing to complain about the meal we got on our flight home last week – flight UZ332. On the booking confirmation it said that we would have breakfast and lunch. Well, breakfast was just a cup of tea and lunch was a tuna sandwich. By itself, this wouldn't have been a problem, but both my husband and I got food poisoning from the sandwich.

4 Now write the final paragraph of the letter, demanding some action from the airline.

Wordbuilding phrasal verbs with *in* and *out*

1 Complete the phrasal verbs using *in* and *out*.

1 Do **drop** ..... and see us the next time you're in town.
2 Stefan **dropped** ..... of college last year because he wanted to travel round the world.
3 Philippa and Sarah used to be business partners but they **fell** ..... over how to develop the business.
4 Chris **fell** ..... with the wrong crowd at college and started missing lectures.
5 Ben is **taking** Greta ..... to that new Thai restaurant tonight.
6 Sorry. Can you speak a little more slowly? I couldn't **take** it all .....
7 I'll **look** ..... and see my parents on my way home to make sure they're OK.
8 **Look** ..... ! You're going to bang your head on that door.
9 Is your old car still going? I thought it would have **given** ..... years ago.
10 I'm trying not to eat sweets, but it's very difficult not to **give** ..... to temptation.

2 Match the phrasal verbs from Exercise 1 with the definitions (a–j).

a have a disagreement .....
b absorb (information) .....
c pay someone a (short) visit .....
d pay someone a (short) visit to check they are all right .....
e become part of a social group .....
f be careful .....
g surrender .....
h arrange a social date with .....
i leave a course before it is finished .....
j stop working or functioning .....

Learning skills writing in English

3 Look at the diagram showing the important elements of writing. Complete the diagram with these elements.

spelling link the ideas action wanted
examples

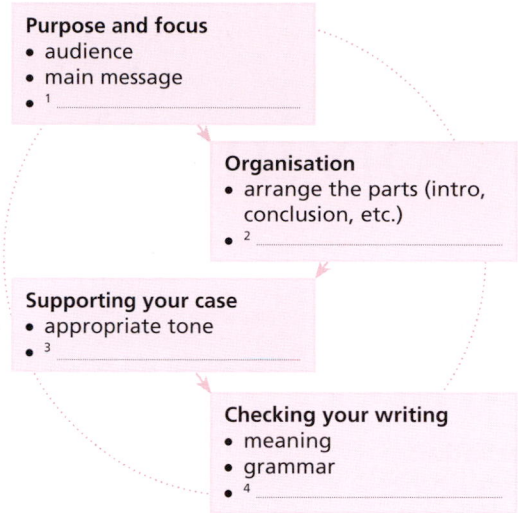

4 Look at the letter of complaint in Exercise 1 on page 50. Answer the questions.

1 What is the main message and where in the letter does this becomes clear?
.....
.....
2 What are the three main elements the letter includes?
.....
3 What phrases does the writer use to link the different ideas?
.....
4 What tone does the writer use?
.....
5 What details make the writer's case more persuasive?
.....

Check!

5 Answer the questions. All the answers are in Student's Book Unit 6.

1 How did Karen Ash have a Japanese holiday without leaving home?
.....
2 What are volunteers helping to build all across North America?
.....
3 Where can you pay to have an uncomfortable night and be treated unkindly?
.....
4 Where can you step right into a painting?
.....
5 What's a way to travel from place to place without ever paying for a bed to sleep in?
.....

Unit 7 Natural resources

7a Solving the water problem

Solving the water problem

Conservation

This is perhaps the simplest and most cost-effective solution. Moreover, everyone can contribute, from the water companies to the end-user. The water companies can make sure that they minimise waste by repairing cracked pipes and by imposing restrictions on water usage – not allowing people to use hosepipes has been one traditional method. But more significantly, they can also limit water consumption by making people pay for what they use, rather than for their connection to the water supply. If everyone had a water meter, they would think more carefully when they turned on the tap. With metered water, the market for water-saving devices – low-flush toilets, efficient washing machines and dishwashers, and water butts for collecting rainwater – will grow by itself.

Desalination

In many parts of the world, there is not enough fresh water but an abundance of salt water. This has encouraged the building of desalination plants. On the face of it, this seems to be a very neat solution. However, these plants are incredibly expensive to build – a recent project in Hawaii cost US $35 million. This is why not many plants have been built in poorer regions. Also, their ecological footprint is heavy. The process requires huge amounts of electricity. There is also growing evidence that the high concentrations of salt which are returned to the earth or the sea have a very damaging effect on plant and wildlife.

New technologies

'Cloud seeding' is a new 'weather modification' technology that scientists are developing to solve global climate change. In this process, the clouds are sprinkled with tiny crystals of silver iodide, which encourage moisture to collect and condense, causing rainfall. Some sceptics wonder whether this technology will be effective and ask what use it is going to be in countries where there is very little cloud. Others worry that no one has properly researched the possible harmful effects of a concentration of silver on human health. As one scientist amusingly put it, 'Sometimes not every cloud has a silver lining.'

The conclusion would seem to be that new technologies are a long way from solving our water problems, particularly in poorer countries. For the moment, conservation still seems to be our best hope.

Reading water

1 Look at the solutions for solving the water problem. Read the text and tick (✓) the solutions that are mentioned.

- ☐ repairing broken water pipes
- ☐ stopping climate change
- ☐ reusing rainwater
- ☐ having fewer showers and baths
- ☐ turning salt water into fresh water
- ☐ making artificial rainclouds

2 Read the article and choose the best option (a–c).

1 Probably the most effective way for water companies to reduce water consumption is:
   a to fix broken water pipes.
   b to limit how much water people are allowed to use.
   c to charge people according to how much water they consume.

2 According to the author, people will buy water-saving devices:
   a if the devices are more efficient.
   b if they see there is financial benefit.
   c whether they have a meter or not.

3 Desalination plants have … main disadvantages.
   a two
   b three
   c four

4 'Cloud seeding' is a technology that:
   a manipulates natural weather patterns.
   b uses the natural elements in a cloud to produce rainfall.
   c encourages cloud formation.

5 The author says that new technologies:
   a will soon be able to provide a solution.
   b will never provide a solution.
   c cannot provide a solution at the moment.

Glossary
moisture (n) /ˈmɔɪstʃə/ water in the air or on the surface of something
restriction (n) /rɪˈstrɪkʃ(ə)n/ limit
sprinkle (v) /ˈsprɪŋkl/ to cover with little pieces of a thing

3 Read the article again and find words that mean:

a a consumer (para 1) .....
b something you use to water the garden or clean the car (para 1) .....
c something that measures the amount of water you consume (para 1) .....
d something that collects water, usually in the garden (para 1) .....
e at first sight (para 2) .....
f impact on the environment (para 2) .....
g a person who isn't convinced (para 3) .....
h 'there is always some good, even in a bad thing' (para 3) .....

Grammar mixed conditional sentences

4 Complete the sentences. Put the verbs in the correct form. Use first, second, third and mixed conditionals.

1 If the water companies ..... (not / impose) restrictions on water use in the past, there ..... (be) water shortages now.
2 If people ..... (have) to pay according to how much water they used, they ..... (use) less water.
3 If companies ..... (introduce) water meters, then people ..... (buy) more water-saving devices.
4 If there ..... (be) more fresh water, we ..... (not/ need) technologies like desalination.
5 If desalination plants ..... (not / be) so expensive, more of them ..... (be built) in poorer countries before now.
6 If some ecosystems ..... (not / be) damaged by pollution, people ..... (feel) more optimistic about this technology.
7 Cloud seeding only ..... (work) if there ..... (be) clouds in the sky.
8 If someone ..... (think) of a better idea than conservation, it ..... (be) in use by now.

5 Pronunciation contractions in conditionals

2.8 Listen to the contracted forms in these sentences. Notice how *I'd have* and *he'd have* sound like one word. Listen again and repeat.

1 If he asked me, I'd certainly offer to help him.
2 I'd come with you, if we could leave a little later.
3 If I'd known, I'd have told you.
4 If he was more thoughtful, he'd have remembered your birthday.
5 If it's not too late to be included, I'd like to come to the meeting.

Vocabulary conservation verbs

6 Complete the sentences about resources using these verbs.

conserve consume preserve protect
run out of save spend waste

1 We've ..... milk. Can you go and buy some from the shop?
2 It's very important to ..... money in good times, so that you have some for the bad times.
3 Don't ..... your energy trying to persuade the council. They are going to build on that green space anyway, even though they promised to ..... it for wildlife.
4 Using salt to ..... food is a very old practice.
5 The WWF has launched a campaign to ..... the tiger from the threat of extinction.
6 We need to return to a simpler way of life. We ..... too much time shopping and we ..... too many goods.

7b Oil

Vocabulary oil

1 Label the pictures using these words.

oil barrel oil field oil pipeline oil refinery
oil rig oil slick oil tanker oil well

1 .....

2 .....

3 .....

4 .....

5 .....

6 .....

7 .....

8 .....

Listening alternatives to oil

2 2.9 Listen to an interview with an oil industry expert. Does he think there is a reasonable alternative to oil?

3 2.9 Listen again and answer the questions.

1 Peak oil means … .
   a the maximum amount of oil that can be extracted
   b the oil which is still in the ground
   c the high point in oil reserves

2 The conventional way to extract oil is to … .
   a drill deep under the surface of the Earth
   b drill a little way under the surface
   c drill only on land

3 The speaker says that unconventional drilling methods can be … .
   a very expensive
   b unsafe
   c not environmentally-friendly

4 What surprises the presenter?
   a that no one has found an alternative to oil
   b that the price of oil continues to rise
   c that people have not chosen another source of fuel

5 What makes petrol so convenient, according to the expert?
   a the amount of energy that petrol produces
   b the easy storage and delivery of petrol
   c both these things

6 What problem do electric cars share with petrol cars?
   a they have a limited range
   b the basic material needed to power them is limited
   c they have the potential to explode

Grammar *wish, would rather* and *if only*

4 Complete these sentences from the interview by putting the verb in the correct form.

1 We wish oil ..... (go) on forever.
2 I wish I ..... (be able) to give you a straight answer.
3 A lot of people wish that we ..... (not / start) to go down this route
4 I'm sure people would rather ..... (have) a cheaper and cleaner alternative.
5 If only there ..... (be) a cheaper, cleaner and more efficient alternative.
6 Would you rather we ..... (run) out of oil or lithium?

5 Complete the short conversations using the correct form of the verbs given.

1 **A**: Would you like to drive or shall I?
B: I'd rather you ..... (drive).
2 **A**: Are you going to buy that new electric car?
B: If only I ..... (have) enough money, then I'd get it tomorrow, but it's over £20,000!
3 **A**: Some people think that cheap petrol is a basic human right.
B: I know. I wish people ..... (stop) complaining and use their cars less.
4 **A**: Your new car is amazing. Doesn't it use a lot of petrol, though?
B: Yes, it does. I wish I ..... (buy) one with a smaller engine.
5 **A**: The oil spill was terrible. What do you think happened to all the oil in the sea?
B: I'd rather ..... (not / think) about it. It's probably still out there.
6 **A**: We all depend too much on the countries who produce oil.
B: I know. I wish each country ..... (become) more independent in its energy needs.
7 **A**: Did you see the programme about alternative energies last night?
B: No, but I wish I ..... (see) it. It looked really interesting.
8 **A**: Shall I speak to the neighbours about parking their car in front of our garage?
B: I'd rather you ..... (not / speak) to them. I don't want to have an argument.

6 **Pronunciation** contractions with *wish* and *would rather*

2.10 Listen to the contracted forms in these sentences. Notice how *I'd = I had* and *I would*, and how *we'd = we had* and *we would*. Listen again and repeat.

1 I wish I'd known earlier.
2 Actually, I'd rather you didn't smoke.
3 If only we'd taken the train.
4 We'd rather not wait, if possible.
5 I wish I'd left my job.

7 **Dictation** Canada's oil sands

2.11 Listen and complete the description of an article about Canada's oil sands.

.....

in the tar sands of Alberta .....

.....

.....

However, ...

.....

.....

as conventional methods of extraction.

As a result, ...

.....

.....

.....

.....

7c An emotive subject

Listening conservation stories

1 2.12 You are going to hear three people talking about conservation projects. Listen and complete the table.

	What needs to be protected?	Has the conservation work been successful?
1	The mangrove ..... in	.....
2	The West African	.....
3	The black poplar ..... in	.....

2 2.12 Listen again. Are the sentences true (T) or false (F)? Or is there not enough information (N) to say if the statements are true or false?

1 Every inhabitant of Cancún misses the beautiful mangrove forest.
2 Waste water has badly damaged the coral reef along this part of the coast.
3 In West Africa, conservationists needed to find out where the giraffe went for food.
4 Farmers were killing the giraffes who fed on their land.
5 People associate the word 'conservation' with work in developing countries.
6 The decrease in the numbers of black poplar trees has been quite sudden.

3 2.12 Complete the sentences about the conservation projects using these words. Then listen and check.

classic heroic rarest rotting sale small wonderful victims

1 Today that forest is buried and ..... underneath 500 hotels.
2 This place is a ..... example of how not to build a tourist resort.
3 Nature is for ..... here.
4 The mangroves are not the only ..... .
5 A ..... effort on the part of conservationists has saved the giraffe.
6 The conservationists could then begin to educate local people about the dangers facing these ..... creatures.
7 But in fact, many conservation efforts are ..... in scale.
8 The black poplar is one of Britain's ..... species of tree.

4 Find words and expressions in Exercise 3 that have these meanings:

1 very typical .....
2 a period of ten years .....
3 a person or thing against which a crime is committed .....
4 placed under the ground .....
5 you can buy it .....
6 decaying or going bad .....

Vocabulary strong feelings

5 Look at these words. Tick the emotive words.

back-breaking criticise deplore desperate interested in keen on majestic obsessed with tall tiring

6 Rewrite the text about the black poplar tree. Replace the words in bold with a more emotive word from the box.

deprived exploit giant most threatened over-developed plummeting rescue wonderful

If you mention the term 'conservation efforts', people often think of attempts to [1] **save** endangered animals; or to protect [2] **poor** communities from [3] **big** corporate organisations which are trying to [4] **use** their land. But in fact, many conservation efforts are small in scale and many have [5] **positive** outcomes. The black poplar tree is one of Britain's [6] **rarest** species and its numbers have been [7] **declining** for decades. That's mainly because much of its natural habitat – the floodplain – has been [8] **built on** with new housing.

1 ..... 5 .....
2 ..... 6 .....
3 ..... 7 .....
4 ..... 8 .....

7d Is globalisation good?

Real life making your point

1 2.13 Listen to four people speaking about globalisation. Are the speakers in favour (F) or against globalisation (A)?

	F	A
Speaker 1	☐	☐
Speaker 2	☐	☐
Speaker 3	☐	☐
Speaker 4	☐	☐

2 2.13 Listen again to the four speakers and complete the summaries.

Speaker 1: Globalisation helps us all to .....

Speaker 2: Globalisation just helps people .....

Speaker 3: Globalisation is just a .....

Speaker 4: Globalisation has just increased .....

3 2.13 Complete these phrases used by the speakers. Then listen and check.

1 That's ..... the ..... .
2 Sorry, I ..... don't ..... that.
3 To ..... , I could live without flowers that are imported from Africa.
4 We're ..... this debate all ..... .
5 ..... if we had to grow our own coffee in England.
6 ..... me ..... you another example.
7 There's no ..... that it has helped the rich.

4 Which techniques did the speakers use in their arguments? Match the speakers (1–4) with the techniques (a–e). There is one extra technique.

Speaker 1 .....
Speaker 2 .....
Speaker 3 .....
Speaker 4 .....

a humour
b challenging the question itself
c speaking clearly and slowly
d illustrating with examples
e anticipating counter-arguments

5 Pronunciation sentence stress

a 2.14 Underline the words that you think are most stressed in these sentences. Then listen and check.

1 Globalisation may have helped the rich, but it hasn't helped the poor. (2 words)
2 Globalisation is not something that has been invented; it's a natural phenomenon. (2 words)
3 I like having things that I can't buy locally, but I don't actually need them. (2 words)
4 Globalisation doesn't harm poor countries; it helps them. (2 words)
5 I wish you were right, but the facts show the opposite. (4 words)

b 2.14 Practise saying the sentences. Listen and compare your pronunciation.

6 Listen and respond making your point

2.15 Listen to a friend asking you to give your opinion about globalisation. Look at the points below. Respond with your own words. Then compare your response with the model answer that follows.

- Stress what your opinion is.
- Reject their argument.
- Give an example.
- Challenge the question itself.

1

What do you think about globalisation?

To be honest with you, I think it's probably a good thing.

7e Waste

Writing a letter to the press

1 Read the letter below and answer the questions

1 What caused the writer to send the letter?

.....

.....

2 What does she say will happen if nothing is done?

.....

.....

Daily Times

Published: January 12

Sir,

I am very tired of seeing so much waste in a world where many people [1] ..... suffer shortages of food, energy and other basic necessities.

Each day at my local supermarket, enormous quantities of food [2] ..... are thrown away when it could easily be given to charities for the homeless. People often throw away electronic equipment, [3] ..... when the item is only four or five years old. Cars [4] ..... sit in traffic jams with their engines running, burning fuel unnecessarily. Clothes, [5] ..... , are so cheap nowadays that people think nothing of wearing something once or twice and then throwing it away.

How have we allowed ourselves to become so careless about precious resources? Are we simply too rich to care? If we do not change the way we behave, a change of behaviour will be forced upon us because there will be no more resources left for us to waste.

H. Henby, Oxford

2 **Writing skills** **giving vivid examples**

a Use these words and one of the details (a–e) to add information that makes the letter more vivid. Insert the information in the spaces (1–5).

such as with especially which who

a items of fashion clothing
b flat-screen TVs, computers or mobile phones
c is near its sell-by date
d live in more difficult circumstances than us
e only one driver in them

b Make the short letter below more vivid by giving more information or examples in the spaces (1–5). Use these notes to help you.

- give more details of the building
- give examples
- describe what people do here
- give examples
- give reasons

Sir,

I agree totally with James Needham (*Daily Times*, 4th May). The decision to build a new block of flats [1] ..... on part of what is now Summerdine Park is shocking. This park not only contains many species of trees [2] ..... , it is also one of the few green spaces in the area, [3] ..... . There are certainly other more suitable places to build new housing [4] ..... . It would be better to develop areas like this [5] ..... .

Word focus *better*

3 Match the beginning of the sentences (1–5) with their endings (a–e).

1 You had better	a than me.
2 We would be better off	b if we kept this car until it gets too expensive to maintain.
3 I think it would be better	c not mention the question of waste to him. He gets very emotional.
4 He always tries to go one better	d than to cut down a tree in a conservation area.
5 He should know better	e to send a letter to the local paper.

4 Complete the dialogue using the verbs in the correct form: *to* + infinitive, infinitive or *-ing*.

Andy: I still haven't heard back from the company that interviewed me last week for a job. Do you think I should call them or would it be better [1] ..... (wait)?

Fran: I think you'd be better off [2] ..... (call) them. It shows you're interested, at least.

Andy: Yeah, you're right. I'd better [3] ..... (do) that this afternoon. It's better [4] ..... (know) than not.

Wordbuilding collocations related to one word

1 Look at these noun + noun collocations. Match them to the definitions below.

air: air bridge air force air vent
water: water jug water leak water lily
wind: wind chill wind farm wind instrument

1 e.g. clarinet, oboe, flute .....
2 used for getting from the airport terminal to the plane .....
3 a place where renewable energy is generated .....
4 the drop in temperature cause by a cold wind .....
5 an escape of water from a pipe or tank .....
6 part of the military, along with the army and navy .....
7 used for serving water at the dinner table .....
8 a place (e.g. in a wall) where air can enter or exit .....
9 a flower that grows in lakes and ponds .....

2 Some noun + noun collocations become one compound noun. Look at these collocations with *sun*. Which two words are opposites?

sunglasses sunlight sunrise sunset suntan

Learning skills improving your listening

3 2.16 A key to understanding fast native speech is to understand stress and linking in English pronunciation. Listen to this sentence and note the stress and linking in it.

1 **Stress**: Sorry I just don't accept that.
2 **Linking**: Sorry‿I just don't‿accept that.

4 2.17 Look at these sentences. Underline the stressed syllables and indicate where the sounds are linked. Then listen and check.

1 Globalisation helps people in rich countries.
2 They can have goods out of season.
3 But to be honest, I don't need flowers imported from Africa in December.

5 2.18 Read these steps for improving your listening skills. Listen again to the first speaker from 7d, Exercise 1 and follow the steps (1–5).

1 Write down the words you hear.
2 Read your transcript back. Does it make grammatical sense?
3 Compare your transcript with the audioscript.
4 Note the words and sounds which have the strongest stress. These should be the key words that convey the meaning.
5 Note which words are clearly linked. This will help you to distinguish them the next time you hear them.

Check!

6 Complete the crossword using phrases about natural resources. All the answers are in Student's Book Unit 10.

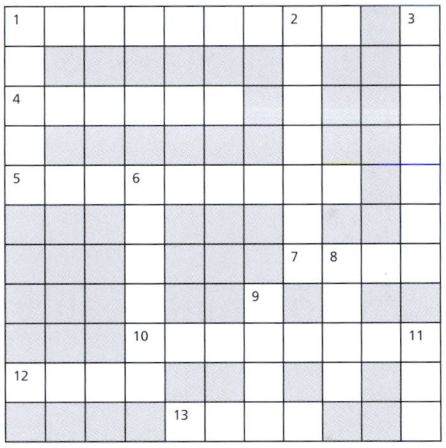

Across
1 resources which can be replaced in nature (9)
4 and 5 with its special plants and wildlife, Madagascar has one of these (6,9)
5 see 4 Across
7 the substance which is removed from water in the desalination process (4)
10 this American river does not reach the sea anymore (8)
12 another word for 'conserve' (4)
13 see 11 Down

Down
1 the three Rs in conservation: reduce, …, recycle (5)
2 people whose job it is to cut down trees (7)
3 Ecuador wanted to be paid not to do this with its oil (7)
6 the opposite of abundant (6)
8 this sea is a tenth of the size it was in the 1960s (4)
9 producing half a kilo of this uses 85,000 litres of water (4)
11 and 13 Across the point where oil is taken from the ground (3, 4)

Unit 8 The news

8a Photojournalism

Vocabulary the news

1 Complete the crossword with words related to news reporting.

Across

1 and 8 a story which is both serious and urgent (4, 4)

3 news which is less serious and not urgent (4)

7 a piece expressing the opinion of the newspaper (9)

Down

2 any piece written in a newspaper or magazine (7)

4 a special or prominent piece in a magazine or newspaper (8)

5 the title of the main news story, written in big letters (8)

6 a section of the newspaper dedicated to a particular writer (6)

	1 H	2 A						
					3 S		4 F	
5 H				6 C				
7 E								
8 N								

Listening re-touching reality

2 2.19 Listen to an interview with a journalist talking about altering photos. What two examples do they discuss? Complete the descriptions.

1 The ..... of the February ..... edition of *National Geographic* magazine.

2 A photo of ..... Reagan and Raisa Gorbachev in *Picture* ..... magazine.

3 2.19 Listen again. Are the sentences true (T) or false (F)?

1 Photo editors changed the size of the pyramids in the photo.

2 An editor said that the changes to the photo were OK because it was a cover photo.

3 He also said that technology had made altering images more acceptable.

4 Editors have said that it's acceptable to alter covers because they advertise the book or magazine.

5 The photographer thinks that there's no difference between manipulating cover images and altering news photos.

6 *Picture Week* changed two photos to suggest the people in them had friendly faces.

7 People thought that the *Picture Week* photo was unacceptable.

8 People are not able to distinguish between reality and fiction.

Glossary

alter (v) /ˈɒltə/ change

digitally enhanced (adj) /ˈdɪdʒɪt(ə)li ɪnˈhɑːnst/ improved using digital technology

touch up (v) /tʌtʃ ˈʌp/ make small changes to improve an image

4 Pronunciation long vowel /əʊ/

2.20 Listen to these words. Pay attention to the long /əʊ/ sound. Then listen again and repeat.

boat	don't	fellow	going	growing	hotel
know	local	opposed	own	photo	sofa

Grammar reporting verbs

5 Rewrite these sentences using the reporting verbs given.

1 People said that the magazine had manipulated reality.
People **accused** the magazine .....
.....

2 The editor said they had altered the image.
The editor **admitted** .....
.....

3 But he said they hadn't done anything wrong.
But he **denied** .....
.....

4 He said modern technology made it easy to alter images.
He **blamed** .....
.....

5 Some editors tell their designers that it is OK to alter images for covers.
Some editors **persuade** .....
.....

6 People complained, saying that they had been given a false impression.
People **complained** .....
.....

7 Some people say, 'Don't trust a photo if there's anything important riding on it.'
Some people **warn** you .....
.....

6 Complete the text using the correct form of the verbs. Use prepositions where necessary.

In the past, photographers have been criticised [1] ..... (invade) people's privacy or [2] ..... (take) pictures that did not reflect the reality of a situation. But nowadays, in the age of digital photography, there is a new problem. How do we know that the photo has not been altered after it has been taken? It would be wrong to blame the photographer [3] ..... (manipulate) some of the photos that appear in our newspapers and magazines. A photo editor might be asked [4] ..... (alter) a photo digitally in order to make a good story. For example, someone might suggest [5] ..... (touch) up the photo of a film star's face to make them look more attractive. Or they might urge the photo editor [6] ..... (add) an image of a frightened child into a photo of a street protest. You can perhaps forgive the editor [7] ..... (make) the first alteration, but what about second? That is a practice people should possibly refuse [8] ..... (accept).

Vocabulary photography

7 Match the verbs in Box A with the nouns in Box B and write the collocations.

A	B
capture	events
open	the lens
record	the moment
see through	a photo
take	a snaphot
take	the shutter

1 .....
2 .....
3 .....
4 .....
5 .....
6 .....

8 Dictation digital photography

2.21 Listen to someone talking about analogue and digital cameras. Then complete the text.

1 Like many of his fellow professionals, photographer Fritz Hoffman .....
.....

2 A digital camera .....
.....
....., but an analogue camera
.....

3 Hoffman also claims .....
.....
.....

4 That's so that .....
.....

8b News in brief

Reading good news stories

1 Read the four newspaper stories below and match the headlines (a–d) with the stories (1–4).

a Better to give than receive
b A sense of community
c A charmed life
d An old secret

2 Write the number of the story (1–4) next to the statements (a–f).

This story shows that:

a you can help people without spending a lot of money. .....
b there is not one right way to do something. .....
c you can inspire other people by your actions. .....
d miracles do happen. .....
e there is a good and a bad side to every situation. .....
f people's faith in human nature can be restored. .....

News in brief

1 .....

In the UK street riots of 2011, it is estimated that rioters caused over £100 million of damage to their own communities. But for every negative, there's often a positive, as the case of Mr Biber, a London barber, shows. Mr Biber's barber shop in London, where he has been cutting hair for 40 years, was among those wrecked, and the 89-year-old thought he had lost everything. But word got around and a website to support him was set up. Donations raised £35,000, enough to make the necessary repairs. Moreover, people's generosity gave Mr Biber the encouragement to carry on doing what he loves.

2 .....

Some people believe that the secret to a long life is a glass of red wine every day. For others, it is plenty of exercise. But few people would claim that eating fast food contributed to longevity. They obviously haven't met 100-year old Catherine Reddoch from Matamata, New Zealand. Every day, using her zimmer frame to support her, she walks a kilometre – a journey which takes her one hour – to her local hamburger café. Here she eats a cheeseburger and drinks a cup of hot chocolate. Mrs Reddoch is not concerned about the fat content of the meal. 'I eat anything and everything – I like my cheeseburgers,' she says. It was reported that on her 100th birthday, the café put a plaque with her name on it on her usual seat.

3 .....

Secret Agent L is the brainchild of one woman, Laura Miller. Laura's mission is to spread kindness in the world. She does this by doing small acts of kindness, like leaving a flower on someone's car windscreen or making a nice walking stick for someone to find when they are on a long walk. The idea is that when someone finds these secret gifts, it brightens up their day. It is believed that Secret Agent L now has over 1,800 followers around the world, all creating and sharing their ideas for similar kind acts.

4 .....

A 21-year-old man who drove his car over the edge of the Grand Canyon escaped with only a few minor injuries. Witnesses said that his car had plunged 200 feet into the mile-deep canyon before hitting a tree which stopped it falling further. It is not thought that he was speeding, but the cause of the accident remains unknown. Another visitor found him lying in the road after he had apparently climbed back out of the canyon. The emergency services said he was an extremely lucky man.

Glossary
plaque (n) /plæk/ a small metal sign
riot (n) /ˈraɪət/ a violent protest

3 Read the stories again and find words that mean:

1 destroyed (para 1) .....
2 gifts of money (para 1) .....
3 living a long time (para 2) .....
4 a walking aid for old people (para 2) .....
5 an original idea (para 3) .....
6 make more cheerful (para 3) .....
7 fell or dived (para 4) .....
8 driving too fast (para 4) .....

Grammar passive reporting verbs

4 Find an example of a passive reporting verb in each story on page 62 and underline it.

5 Grammar extra tenses in passive reporting verbs

▶ TENSES IN PASSIVE REPORTING VERBS

Note how these tenses are transformed from active to passive.

People say ...	→	*It is said that ...*
People have said ...	→	*It has been said that ...*
People said ...	→	*It was said that ...*
People had said ...	→	*It had been said that ...*

Look at the grammar box. Rewrite these phrases using passive reporting verbs.

1 People say that ... → It *is said that ...*
2 Everyone understands that ...
It .....
3 Everyone knew that ...
It .....
4 People believed that ...
It .....
5 People have estimated that ...
It .....
6 People think that ...
It .....
7 People had hoped that ...
It .....
8 Everyone supposes that ...
It .....

6 Rewrite the sentences using passive reporting verbs.

1 People say that for every negative, there is always a positive.
It is said that for every negative, there is always a positive.
2 People expect Mr Biber to carry on doing what he loves.
It ..... that Mr Biber ..... what he loves.
3 People used to think that a glass of red wine a day helped you to live longer.
In the past, ...
4 Most people don't recommend eating fast food if you want to live longer.
It ..... that you .....
5 People hoped that secret gifts would brighten up someone's day.
It ..... that secret gifts .....
6 People supposed that the tree prevented the car falling further.
It .....
7 People considered the man lucky to survive the accident.
It ..... that the man .....
8 People have reported great success with the idea.
It ..... the idea ..... very successful

Vocabulary the feel-good factor

7 Match the adjectives describing good news stories in box A with the words that have the opposite or a near opposite meaning in box B.

A	B
amusing	ordinary
charming	depressing
inspiring	pessimistic
quirky	serious
encouraging	dreary
optimistic	uninspiring

8 Pronunciation weak forms in verbs

2.22 Listen to the auxiliary verbs in these sentences. Note how they are pronounced using the weak form. Listen again and repeat.

1 It was estimated that £100 million worth of damage was caused in the riots.
2 It is believed that Secret Agent L has more than 200 followers.
3 It was thought that the driver had fallen asleep at the wheel of his car.
4 It was expected that the injured man would make a full recovery.
5 It has been estimated that 50% of the population will be overweight by 2020.
6 It had been thought that diet was more important than exercise.

8c Balanced reporting

Listening news reports

1 2.23 Listen to a journalist talking about balanced reporting. Are the sentences true (T) or false (F)?

1 *National Geographic* likes to report on endangered environments.
2 The main article was about a gas pipeline.
3 The speaker thinks that journalists should give equal space to both sides in a debate.

2 2.23 Listen to the report again and choose the correct option.

1 Journalists have to try to give a balanced *view / opinion* and tell a good story.
2 *National Geographic* tries to find places where we can marvel at the *joys / wonders* of nature.
3 The main article described the *beauty / nature* of the white Kermode Spirit Bear.
4 A smaller article described the building of a gas *platform / pipeline.*
5 *Technically / Strictly* speaking, it was inaccurate to say the government had given its approval.
6 The journalists and editors in question *shot / jumped* the gun in order to make their point.
7 The article highlights the *dilemma / problem* for journalists.
8 Ideally the people involved would like to have *the say-so / the last word.*

3 Look at the words and expressions in Exercise 2 and find words that mean:

1 in actual fact (2 words) .....
2 amazing and beautiful things (1 word) .....
3 have the final decision (4 words) .....
4 an impartial opinion (2 words) .....
5 a difficult choice (1 word) .....
6 be too hasty (3 words) .....

Word focus *word*

4 Look at these expressions with *word* and choose the correct definition (a or b).

1 *From the word go,* the restaurant was full every night.
   a from when we had permission
   b from the start
2 Jamie has been behaving very strangely recently. Can you *have a quiet word with* him?
   a be very strict with b talk privately to
3 Please *don't say a word* to Sarah about the cup I broke. It's her favourite.
   a don't mention b lie
4 He said I would never be a professional artist but he had to *eat his words.*
   a admit he was wrong b apologise

5 Complete the sentences using the expressions with *word.*

don't take my word for it eat my words
from the word go gave his word
have the last word
one person's word against another's
was lost for words word of mouth

1 Our magazine gets most of its new customers by ..... or because someone has read a copy in a doctor's waiting room.
2 I assured them that it would be easy to find a good wildlife photographer. I hope I don't have to ..... .
3 It is just ..... . In the end, the reader will have to decide who they believe.
4 If you don't believe what I'm telling you, then ..... . Go and check the facts for yourself.
5 He ..... that he would not publish the story before I had read it.
6 ....., the journalist involved the company in the research for the article.
7 I didn't know what to say – I ..... .
8 She's very argumentative and always has to ..... .

8d Guess what

Real life reporting what you heard

1 Complete the sentences. Use a verb in each space. Do the sentences express belief (B) or disbelief (D)?

	B	D
1 I think I'd ..... her word for it.	☐	☐
2 He generally ..... his facts right.	☐	☐
3 He's not the type to ..... gossip.	☐	☐
4 ..... no notice of what she says.	☐	☐
5 It's been ..... out of proportion.	☐	☐
6 I'd ..... that with a pinch of salt.	☐	☐

2 2.24 Listen to a conversation between two friends, Jane and Annie, and answer the questions.

1 What is the news about Patrick that Jane wants to share?

.....

.....

.....

2 Who did she hear this news from?

.....

3 What does Annie ask Jane to do with the news? Why?

.....

.....

3 2.24 Complete the sentences from the conversation. Then listen again and check.

verbs: guess heard reckons seems
prepositions: about according to
adverbs: apparently supposedly
nouns: gossip pinch

1 Did you hear the good news ..... (*preposition*) Patrick? ..... (*verb*) what?
2 Well, ... (*adverb*) he was spotted by someone from a big theatrical agency.
3 She ..... (*verb*) that it won't be long before we see him on TV.
4 Well, I'd take that with a ..... (*noun*) of salt if I were you.
5 No, ... (*preposition*) Kate, it's more than that.
6 That'd be fantastic. I ..... (*verb*) that it was really difficult to get that kind of work.
7 Don't worry. I'm not the type to spread ..... (*noun*). Does the agency take a big fee?
8 It ..... (*verb*) that they only take 10% or 15%, ... (*adverb*).

4 Pronunciation the schwa

2.25 Listen to these words from the conversation. Underline the stressed syllable and circle the schwa / ə / sounds.
Example: s(u)ppos(e)dly

1 comedy	5 according
2 festival	6 difficult
3 apparently	7 agency
4 reckon	8 theatrical

5 Listen and respond reporting what you heard

2.26 Listen to someone giving you some news about government taxes. Respond after the tone with your own words. Then compare your response with the model answer that follows.

1 *Did you hear the good news about taxes?*

Good news about taxes? No, what happened?

8e Group action

Vocabulary meetings

1 Write two verbs that collocate with each noun.

attend discuss draft hold make (x2)
put forward reach weigh up write

1 ....., ...
a meeting

2 ....., ...
a suggestion

3 ....., ...
a decision

4 ....., ...
the options

5 ....., ...
a letter

2 **Writing skill impersonal language**

Rewrite the sentences using impersonal language. Use the words given.

1 We all got together to discuss how to raise the money.
A ..... (held)

2 We discussed all the things that we could do.
All ..... (options)

3 Julian suggested that we should ask the local council for help.
One ..... (suggestion)

4 Pete said it was better to have some fun events.
Another ..... (idea)

5 Several people said organising events would take too long.
It ..... (agreed)

6 No one could decide what to do about funding the project.
..... (decision)

Writing minutes from a meeting

3 Read the minutes from a local meeting about a waste incinerator (a plant where rubbish is burned) in the area. Answer the questions.

1 What are the main advantages and disadvantages of the incinerator? .....
.....
.....

2 What action was decided on? .....
.....

3 What action was rejected? .....
.....

St Paul's Residents' Association

From: Kathy Barbosa

Re: New waste incinerator

Here are the minutes from the meeting which was held on 3 September.

- Following the government's decision to build a new waste incinerator on the old factory site in Quibble Street, we met to decide what action residents could take to oppose this new source of pollution.
- Karen suggested that we should get everyone in the area to sign a petition against the proposal. Everyone agreed that this was a good first step.
- Tom thought we should present the government with some alternative locations, but no one at the meeting was able to suggest any so the action was rejected.
- Jo made the point that the government wanted to use the incinerator to generate electricity for the area, which was a good thing for the community.
- Kevin proposed that we could have another kind of plant which sorted the waste for recycling. Harry said he would research this option and discuss it at the next meeting.

Next meeting date: **26 September**

4 Replace the underlined phrases with more impersonal ones.

1 *a meeting was held to decide* .....
2 .....
3 .....
4 .....
5 .....
6 .....
7 .....

Wordbuilding forming adjectives from verbs

1 Complete the sentences using the verbs + *-ing*.

charm confuse depress inspire
refresh tire touch worry

1 It is ..... that she is so late – she's normally very punctual.
2 The article was rather ..... . You couldn't work out why the daughter had left her family.
3 It's very ..... to hear a story about a business which doesn't just do things to make money.
4 He is a really ..... man – polite, interesting and kind.
5 The story about two friends overcoming their difficulties was very ..... .
6 Environmental news is often ..... , but in this case the story offered hope.
7 The news featured the ..... story of a 14-year-old girl who got a part-time job to help support her family.
8 It's very ..... to follow a film with subtitles for three hours.

2 Make adjectives using verbs + *-ive*.

1 good at **inventing** *inventive* (from *invent*)
2 good at **persuading** .....
3 good at **creating** .....
4 liking to **compete** .....
5 **producing** a lot .....
6 **talking** a lot .....
7 wanting to **protect** .....
8 not **responding** .....

Learning skills keeping a learning diary

3 What is a learning diary and why is it a good idea to keep one? Look at these reasons and compare them with your own ideas.

- To learn from your mistakes and your successes
- To track your progress
- To make clear targets for the next stage of your learning
- To record what you have learnt

4 Read the following actions which can help you to evaluate and personalise your learning.

Actions

1 Write down your experiences of learning after each lesson: what you found easy, what you found difficult, what was the most important thing you learned.

2 Note down mistakes that you have made before.

3 Make a note of an extract, even a sentence, that you particularly liked and try to memorise it.

4 Set yourself a small task based on the language you learned in your last lesson, e.g. describe a good news story, report what someone said to you, or describe a situation where somebody's reputation was questioned.

5 Apply the actions (1–4) for Unit 8. Then remember to do it for your next lesson!

Check!

6 Do the quiz. You can find all the answers in Student's Book Unit 8.

Quiz Time

1 Complete these quotations.
a 'A picture is worth a thousand w..... .'
b 'Good news doesn't s..... .'
c 'Bad news travels f..... .'

2 Complete these sentences about the characters in Unit 8.
a The pilot Peter Burkill went from hero to z..... .
b Sharbat Gula's photo is one of the most i..... images of our time.
c It was believed that the large blue butterfly was e..... in Britain.

3 Complete the phrases about the news.
a The best form of advertising is when news travels by word of m..... .
b Good news stories generate a f..... factor among people.
c It's not a good thing to s..... gossip.
d There was an amazing f..... about India in National Geographic this month.

Unit 9 Talented people

9a The great communicator

Listening

1 2.27 Read the questions. Then listen to the description of Ronald Reagan and complete the answers.

1 Where was Ronald Reagan raised?
In a .....

2 What was jobs did he have before he entered politics?
He worked as a .....
and .....

3 What important historical event occurred during his presidency?
The collapse of .....

4 How did people make fun of him as President?
They said he .....

5 What made him a great communicator?
His ability to .....

6 What other factor worked in his favour as president?
It was a time of .....

2 2.27 Look at the words and phrases in bold from the description of Ronald Reagan. Choose the correct meaning (a or b). Then listen again and check.

1 His skills as **an orator** were noticed and he was persuaded to run for Governor of California.
a a politician
b a public speaker

2 He took a **hard line** against communism.
a strict approach
b difficult road

3 He understood the **fundamental essence** of leadership.
a real meaning
b basic problem

4 He made people feel that they **mattered**.
a were lucky
b were important

5 The economy **thrived** during his presidency.
a did badly
b did well

6 Reagan's style of communication **stands out**.
a is noticeable
b is old-fashioned

Vocabulary careers

3 2.27 Complete the sentences with the correct verb. Then listen again to the description and check your answers.

1 Ronald Reagan ..... from Eureka College, Illinois with a degree in economics and sociology.

2 He ..... for a short while as a radio broadcaster in Iowa.

3 He moved to Los Angeles to ..... a career as an actor in films and television.

4 After ..... the Republican Party in 1962, his skills as an orator were noticed.

5 He ..... a good job as Governor of California.

6 He went on to ..... President of the United States between 1981 and 1989.

Grammar articles: *the* or zero article?

4 Complete with *the* or zero article (–).

Countries: ..... Japan, ... United Arab Emirates, ... Netherlands, ... Thailand

Places: ..... Amazon River, ... countryside, ... Moon, ... Mount Everest

Times: ..... weekend, ... Saturday, ... April, ... spring

Other: ..... breakfast, ... police, ... poor, ... biology

5 Complete the sentences with *the* or zero article (–).

1 After joining ..... Republican Party in 1962, his skills as an orator were noticed and he was persuaded to run for ..... Governor of ..... California.

2 He then went on to become President of ..... United States between ..... 1981 and 1989.

3 He remains one of ..... most popular American presidents of ..... past 50 years.

4 Ronald Reagan understood ..... fundamental essence of ..... leadership: that is, that you have to be able to communicate.

5 Reagan always gave ..... impression that he was listening when he was speaking to you.

6 He looked you in ..... eye, smiled at you, made you feel special.

7 He presided over a time of ..... great economic growth in ..... America.

8 ..... things weren't great for most Americans and he gave them ..... hope.

9 It obviously helped that ..... economy thrived during his presidency.

10 If you can connect with ..... ordinary person, there's very little you can do wrong.

6 Pronunciation linking vowels

a 2.28 Listen to these phrases. What sound links the words: /w/, /j/ or /r/?

	/w/	/j/	/r/
1 one idea‿at a time	☐	☐	☐
2 he‿often spoke to ordinary people	☐	☐	☐
3 do‿a good job	☐	☐	☐
4 the beginning of the‿end	☐	☐	☐
5 an area‿of outstanding beauty	☐	☐	☐
6 China‿and India	☐	☐	☐
7 look someone in the‿eye	☐	☐	☐
8 too‿expensive	☐	☐	☐
9 it's so‿exciting	☐	☐	☐

b 2.28 Listen again and check. Then practise saying each phrase.

7 Dictation careers

2.29 Listen to three people describing their careers. Write down the words you hear. Be careful – many of the sentences contain the linking sounds /w/, /j/ or /r/.

1 I guess I .....

.....

.....

.....

2 It's not easy .....

.....

.....

.....

3 I was always told .....

.....

.....

.....

Vocabulary qualifications

8 Complete the job interview between an interviewer (I) and an applicant (A) using these words.

background experience knowledge
qualifications qualities talents

I: So can you tell me first a little bit about your [1] ..... ?

A: Sure. My mother's French and my father's English. I was brought up in France and …

I: And do you have any previous [2] ..... of journalism?

A: Yes. At university I was editor of the student magazine and after that I worked for a local radio station …

I: What [3] ..... do you have?

A: I have a degree in media studies and a diploma in …

I: What would you say are your best [4] ..... ?

A: I'm a very organised person, I'm hard-working and I think I …

I: Do you have any [5] ..... of European politics?

A: Well, I read the papers regularly and I take a great interest in current affairs …

I: And lastly. Do you have any particular [6] ..... ? Things that might make you different other candidates?

A: I'm good at learning languages and I'm a good photographer.

9b An inspirational scientist

Reading

1 Read the text quickly and underline the part of the text that answers these questions.

1 What is the aim of Hayat Sindi's work?
2 What is the problem with medicines used to fight diseases like hepatitis?
3 What is the tool that can prevent this?
4 Why did Sindi move to England?
5 What is her hope for other women like her?

2 Read the text again and answer the questions. Choose the correct option (a–c).

1 Which of the following is NOT a quality of the new tool?
a small b powerful c high-tech
2 Where is more health monitoring needed?
a in developed countries
b in developing countries
c everywhere
3 Compared to results from a diagnostic laboratory, this tool's results are … .
a more accurate b more positive
c quicker
4 Sindi's family was not … .
a rich b academic c traditional
5 Sindi studied hard in England because she was afraid of … .
a her parents b failure c feeling lonely
6 Sindi would like women to use their education to … .
a go abroad
b help their own countries
c become scientists

3 Look at these words and phrases from the text. Choose the best definition (a–c).

1 entire (para 1)
a complete b modern c sophisticated
2 detect (para 2)
a have b find c solve
3 low-tech (para 2)
a cheap b small c not sophisticated
4 daunting (para 3)
a medical b very difficult
c personal
5 against the odds (para 3)
a unsurprisingly b unfairly
c unexpectedly
6 guidance (para 4)
a teaching b comfort c advice

Something the size of a postage stamp, costing just a penny apiece, could be a medical breakthrough that will save millions of lives. According to biotechnology scientist Hayat Sindi, this tiny piece of paper has the same power as an entire diagnostic laboratory. 'My mission is to find simple, inexpensive ways to monitor health,' Sindi says. She believes technology pioneered by a team at Harvard University will make it possible, and she co-founded the charity 'Diagnostics For All' to produce and distribute the innovation.

In the developing world, powerful drugs are used to combat diseases like HIV/AIDS, tuberculosis and hepatitis. But these medicines can cause liver damage. In developed countries, doctors monitor liver function frequently and change the medication if they detect problems. But in isolated, rural corners of the world, health monitoring simply doesn't exist. The tragic result is that millions are dying from the same drugs intended to save them. The small piece of paper is a low-tech tool which detects disease by analysing bodily fluids. Positive results, which show up in less than a minute, are indicated by a change in colour on the paper.

Sindi's determination to solve daunting problems should come as no surprise. Despite coming from a modest background, never travelling outside Saudi Arabia or speaking a word of English, she moved to England to attend university. Alone, homesick, and worried that she would fail and dishonour her family, she learned English by watching BBC news. She studied up to 20 hours a day for college entrance exams. Against the odds, she became the first Saudi woman to study biotechnology at Cambridge University. She went on to get a PhD and become a visiting scholar at Harvard University.

Sindi's passion and accomplishments have made her a role model for young women across the Middle East, an inspiration to a new generation. 'I want all women to believe in themselves and know they can transform society. When I lecture at schools, the first thing I ask children is to draw a picture of a scientist. 99.9% of them draw an old bald man with glasses. When I tell them I'm a scientist, they look so surprised.' A new foundation that she has launched gives guidance and money to encourage young women who attend university abroad to bring their skills back to their homelands.

Grammar relative clauses and reduced relative clauses

4 Look at the article again and find examples of the following.

1 a defining relative clause using *which* (para 2)

.....

2 a defining relative clause using *who* (para 4)

.....

3 a non-defining relative clause using *which* (para 2) .....

4 a reduced relative clause using a present participle (para 1) .....

5 a reduced relative clause using a past participle (para 1) .....

5 Write sentences using relative clauses. Use the relative pronouns *who, which, whose, where* and *when*. Use commas where necessary.

1 The piece of paper is the size of a postage stamp. It could save thousands of lives.

.....

.....

2 The charity 'Diagnostics for All' produces the tool. It was co-founded by Sindi.

.....

.....

3 The tool will be used in developing countries. It is difficult to find clinics there.

.....

.....

4 People take powerful drugs to combat diseases. These drugs can cause liver damage.

.....

.....

5 The results show up on the paper. The paper's colour changes if there is a problem.

.....

.....

6 Sindi went to England. She was a young woman at the time.

.....

.....

7 Sindi later went to Harvard. She was the first Saudi woman to study biotechnology at Cambridge.

.....

.....

8 Sindi has become a role model for other women. They want to follow her example.

.....

.....

6 Replace the relative clauses in these sentences with reduced relative clauses. Number 6 has two clauses.

1 Sindi's low-tech tool helps people who are suffering from the negative effects of the drugs.

.....

2 People who live far away from hospitals and clinics will benefit from this technology.

.....

3 The same medicines, which have been designed to fight disease, can also harm people.

.....

4 Sindi, who was determined to succeed, studied up to twenty hours a day.

.....

5 Sindi uses her own experience to inspire other women who wish to become scientists.

.....

6 A new foundation, which was launched recently by Sindi, offers help to young women who want to follow a career in science.

.....

.....

Vocabulary personal qualities

7 The adjectives below describe Sindi's qualities. Find the nouns in the article from which the adjectives are derived.

	Adjective	Noun
1	determined	.....
2	accomplished	.....
3	inspirational	.....
4	passionate	.....

8 Complete the summary about Sindi Hayat. Use these adjectives.

adaptable analytical articulate daring
easy-going independent passionate patient

Sindi Hayat is [1] ..... about helping people in developing countries. She also is an [2] ..... speaker and supporter of women's right to education. To be a scientist, you have to have an [3] ..... mind and to be very [4] ....., as it can take a long time to get positive results from an experiment.

Sindi has an [5] ..... spirit, demonstrated by the fact that she went to England alone to study at university. Living in a different culture also requires you to be [6] ..... For Sindi, to take these risks showed what a [7] ..... individual she is. Despite everything, Sindi remains a very relaxed and [8] ..... person.

9c Women leaders

Listening

1 2.30 Look at the qualities of leaders below. Which do you associate with men (M) and which with women (W)? Listen to an interview with an author and check.

	M	W
1 happy to take risks	☐	☐
2 good at getting things done	☐	☐
3 care more what others think	☐	☐
4 insisting on a point	☐	☐
5 good at persuading people	☐	☐
6 giving orders	☐	☐
7 including others in decisions	☐	☐
8 good organisers	☐	☐

2 2.30 Listen again. Are the sentences true (T) or false (F)?

1 The interviewer thinks that whether a leader is male or female is not the issue.
2 The author says that her claims are supported by research.
3 The author is surprised that women, not men, take more risks.
4 According to the author, men care more about what others around them think.
5 The interviewer thinks that the author is stereotyping women.
6 The author thinks that people want a more co-operative style of leadership than in the past.

3 2.30 Complete the adjectives to describe the qualities in Exercise 1. Then listen and check.

1 adventur.....
2 effect.....
3 sensi.....
4 car.....
5 assert.....
6 persuas.....
7 autocrat.....
8 inclu.....

4 **Pronunciation** **word stress in adjectives ending *-ive***

a 2.31 Listen to the adjective words ending *-ive* from Exercise 3. The stress falls in the same place in each one, except for one word. What rule can you make? Which is the odd one out?

b 2.32 Look at these adjectives. Listen and underlined the stressed syllable.

1 protective
2 creative
3 perceptive
4 imaginative
5 responsive
6 impulsive

Word focus *long*

5 Look at the sentence from the interview and its definition. Then match the sentences (1–10) with the correct definition (a–j).

It doesn't matter what gender a leader is, **as long as** they are a good leader.
= It doesn't matter what gender a leader is, **if/provided that** they are a good leader.

1 'It's been great to see you. I hope we can meet up again **before long**.'
2 He stood there for what seemed like hours and **at long last** someone opened the door.
3 She wasn't angry that the company paid her poorly, but she **longed for** recognition.
4 They arrived **long after** they had intended to.
5 Jake and I **go back a long way**.
6 **The long and short of it** is that we need to reduce our spending or we'll be in trouble.
7 He **put on a long face**, so I asked him what the matter was.
8 He **has come a long way** since he was working as a washer-up in his local café.
9 '**So long**,' she said, 'I'll write to you soon.'
10 **In the long term,** I think we will see benefits from all these efficiencies.

a after much waiting
b are old friends
c desired very much
d goodbye
e the main message
f looked sad
g made a lot of progress
h much later than
i over a long period of time
j soon

9d Your own talents

Real life describing skills, talents and experience

1 Complete these expressions using the correct preposition.

1 At university, I specialised ..... photojournalism.
2 I'm very familiar ..... your magazine.
3 I'm good ..... spotting an interesting story.
4 I have some experience ..... news photography.
5 I think I'd be suited ..... working in this kind of environment.
6 I feel quite comfortable ..... tight deadlines.
7 I'm very keen ..... the idea of working closely with other journalists.
8 I'm serious ..... wanting to become a full-time news photographer.

2 2.33 Listen to three people describing their skills at a job interview. What job are they applying for?

.....

.....

3 2.33 Listen again and answer the questions about each of the applicants.

1 What are the skills or talents of each applicant?

Applicant 1

.....

.....

Applicant 2

.....

.....

Applicant 3

.....

.....

2 What does each speaker lack experience of?

Applicant 1

.....

.....

Applicant 2

.....

.....

Applicant 3

.....

.....

4 Grammar extra adjective + *-ing* or *to* + infinitive

▶ ADJECTIVE + *ING* or *TO* + INFINITIVE

Some adjectives can be followed by a preposition + *-ing* or by an infinitive.

*I'm interested **in learning** French.*
*I'm happy **to show** you how it works.*

Look at the grammar box. Complete the sentences. Use the correct form of the verb: *-ing* form or *to* + infinitive.

1 I'd be keen on ..... (participate) in one of your trial days.
2 I'll be sad ..... (leave) this place.
3 I'm interested in ..... (travel) to new places.
4 I'm excited about ..... (do) field research in India.
5 I'm very keen ..... (work) abroad.
6 I'd be interested ..... (find out) more about the job.

5 Pronunciation difficult words

2.34 Practise saying these pairs of words. Then listen and check your pronunciation.

1 although also
2 clothes cloth
3 private privacy
4 knowledge know-how
5 suit sweet
6 island Iceland
7 receipt recipe
8 thorough through

6 Listen and respond describing skills, talents and experience

2.35 Listen to questions at an interview for a job as a journalist with a local newspaper. Respond with your own words. Then compare your response with the model answer that follows.

1

So what did you study at university?

I studied media, but I specialised in newspaper journalism.

9e Networking

Writing an online profile

1 Complete the personal profile using the information below (a–f).

a Current
b Freelance marketing consultant and translator
c London Business School, UK
d Media and food
e Summary
f Past

Mitsuko Uchida

1 .....

Location: Tokyo
Industry: 2 .....
3 ..... : Advising British supermarket on market plan for Japan

4 ..... :

- Marketing Manager, Disney, Japan – responsible for 'Winnie the Pooh' account;
- Marketing assistant, Coca Cola, Japan;
- Translated marketing documents for various British and US companies.

Education:
Seisen International School; Tokyo University;
5 .....
Currently doing distance learning MBA.

6 .....
I love projects which combine my language skills with my experience in marketing. I am interested in cross-cultural issues and in fun or exciting marketing projects. You can see some examples of my work by clicking on the links below.

2 Answer the questions.

1 What kind of work is Mitsuko interested in? .....
2 What languages can she speak? .....
3 How would you describe her level of education? .....

3 Writing skill writing in note form

a Look at these shortened phrases from the profile and put them into full sentences.

1 advising British supermarket on market plan for Japan
.....
2 responsible for 'Winnie the Pooh' account
.....
3 translated marketing documents for various British and US companies
.....
4 currently doing distance learning MBA
.....

b The personal profile below has no shortened phrases. Find the places where it would be appropriate to use them and rewrite the sentences in a shortened form.

Harry Ross

I am a specialist website designer
.....

Current: I am designing an interactive website for a local sports and leisure centre.
.....

Work history: I used to work for British Telecom as a computer programmer. Afterwards I worked for a local hospital designing their patient communications website. I set up my own company in 2010.
.....
.....
.....

Education: I went to Buckingham Grammar School and Liverpool University.
.....
.....

I specialise in websites that use video and special effects. I think that most websites are too static and my aim is to create websites that are fun and exciting to use. I have many good recommendations from customers and you can see some of the websites I have created by clicking on the links below.

Wordbuilding verb (+ preposition) + noun collocations

1 In each of these groups, one of the verbs does NOT collocate with the noun on the right. Put a line through this verb.

1	follow/do/have	a career
2	make/do/attend	a course
3	acquire/learn/get	a skill
4	take/make/pass	an exam
5	get/win/acquire	promotion
6	gain/win/get	experience
7	own/have/nurture	a talent
8	do/work/get	a job
9	gain/earn/get	a qualification
10	join/set up/take on	a company

2 Complete the description of someone's career by putting a suitable verb in each space.

When I was 19 I [1] ..... an exam to get into a drama school in London, but I was unsuccessful. At that point, I had to decide whether to try to [2] ..... a career in acting or just abandon the idea and [3] ..... a completely different kind of job. All my friends told me that I [4] ..... a natural talent for acting and that I didn't need to [5] ..... a qualification to prove it. So instead, I [6] ..... a small theatre company and [7] ..... experience of acting that way. Just by working with other actors I was able to [8] ..... new skills and two years ago I was asked by the National Theatre to perform in a production of Shakespeare's *The Tempest*. I have never looked back!

Learning skills the language of learning

3 When you learn a language, you often need to ask questions about it. Look at the terms (1–8). Then match the terms with the definitions (a–h).

1 a part of speech
2 past participle
3 an idiom
4 a colloquial expression
5 a false friend
6 a collocation
7 register
8 a euphemism

a two words that naturally go together
b a phrase whose meaning is not clear from the individual words it is composed of
c the level of formality
d e.g. noun, verb, adjective, adverb, preposition
e a word that looks similar in two languages but has different meanings
f the third form of the verb, e.g. 'go, went, gone'
g a word or phrase that expresses an idea more politely or gently
h a phrase used in everyday informal speech

4 Answer these questions about words from Unit 9.

1 What is the past participle of *feel*? .....
2 What part of speech is *the*? .....
3 What verb collocates with *knowledge*? .....
4 Is *grab someone's attention* an idiom? .....
5 What register is the online profile on page 74 of the Workbook? .....

Check!

5 Answer these questions. You can find all the answers in Student's Book Unit 9.

1 What are these people's jobs?

a ..... b .....

2 Complete this famous quotation of Neil Armstrong.

'That's one small ..... for man, one giant ..... for ..... .'

3 Which of these places have *the* in front of them?
a ..... Atlantic Ocean
b ..... Korea
c ..... Florida
d ..... USA
e ..... Moon

4 What type of clause is the underlined clause in the quotation?
a a defining relative clause
b a non-defining relative clause
c a reduced relative clause

Kira Salak, known as the real-life Lara Croft, doesn't want to tell travel stories you have already heard.

Unit 10 Customs and behaviour

10a Child behaviour

Listening growing up

1 2.36 Listen to four people talking about growing up and child behaviour. Match the speakers (1–4) with the topic they are talking about (a–f). There are two extra topics.

Speaker 1 .....
Speaker 2 .....
Speaker 3 .....
Speaker 4 .....

a Being the youngest in the family
b Being the eldest
c Learning from each other
d Sibling rivalry
e Home schooling
f Discipline in the home

Glossary
intervene (v) /ˌɪntəˈviːn/ get involved
sibling (n) /ˈsɪblɪŋ/ a brother or sister

2 2.36 Listen again. Write the number of the speaker (1–4) next to the view they are expressing.

a Family arguments are perfectly healthy. .....
b The best results are when children learn for themselves. .....
c Having to fight to get your parents' attention can have a positive effect. .....
d Children need to mix with lots of other children. .....
e Your position in the family – e.g. first child, second child – is influential. .....
f Parents should try to be less involved in their children's upbringing. .....

3 Look at the words and phrases in bold from the interviews and choose the correct definition.

1 Schools don't **stretch** children enough.
a discipline
b challenge
c teach

2 I'm sure they **mean well**, but they're missing the point.
a have good intentions
b have good ideas
c have good qualities

3 Children often **squabble** over toys.
a have small arguments
b lose interest
c make friendships

4 Eldest children are organising and **bossy** types.
a showing leadership qualities
b independent
c telling others what to do

5 Younger children are often the **clowns** of the family.
a ones who aren't taken seriously
b ones who like to joke
c the less intelligent ones

6 It's normal just to leave the children to **get on with it**.
a manage by themselves
b make friends with each other
c grow up

Grammar habitual actions: present tenses, *will*

4 Complete the short passages about growing up and child behaviour. Use the present simple, present continuous and *will*.

1
Some parents [1] ..... (take) their children out of school because they [2] ..... (think) that they are not being challenged enough. These parents then [3] ..... (teach) their children at home, giving them structured lessons each day. Some [4] ..... (follow) a programme specially written for home schooling, others [5] ..... (design) their own programme of lessons and activities.

2
Parents complain that their children [6] ..... (always / fight) and [7] ..... (squabble). It is of course the case that most children do this when they are young. Even older siblings [8] ..... (argue) and fight as they struggle for their parents' approval. But psychologists [9] ..... (say) that this is normal behaviour and it [10] ..... (help) to prepare them for other relationships later in life.

3
There is quite a lot of literature written about the personality traits of children according to their birth order. First-borns [11] ..... (tend) to be model children: conscientious and reliable and high-achievers. They [12] ..... (generally / follow) a career that their parents approve of and [13] ..... (be) successful at it. Middle children are more difficult to categorise, but they [14] ..... (always / follow) a different path from their elder brother or sister. Last-borns are sociable and fun-loving and [15] ..... (often / get) all the attention when in a group.

5 Look at these examples of annoying behaviour. Complete the sentences using the present continuous with *always* of the verbs.

ask leave play spend ~~talk~~ talk

1 A girl is on her mobile phone all the time.
She*'s always talking* to her friends on the phone.
2 In the car, a young boy says: 'Are we nearly there yet?'
He ..... we're nearly there yet.
3 A teenage girl spends ages in the bathroom so no one else in the family can get in.
She ..... in the bathroom.
4 At mealtimes, a young boy never swallows his food before speaking.
He ..... with his mouth full.
5 A teenage boy is obsessed with computer games.
He ..... computer games.
6 A young girl never tidies her bedroom up.
She ..... her room in a mess.

Vocabulary raising children: verbs

6 Complete the sentences using the correct verbs. The first letter has been given for you.

My father worked abroad for most of my childhood so we were [1] **b**..... up by my mother. When he came home, he used to [2] **s**..... us quite a lot, buying us presents and taking us out. He never [3] **p**..... us if we were naughty, because he wanted enjoy to his time with. He left it to my mum to [4] **d**..... us. That was tough on her, because we used to [5] **d**..... her quite a lot – playing outside when she had told us not to.

It's difficult to be a single parent looking after your children. You are always [6] **n**..... them to do things, when really you want to enjoy the time you have with them. My elder sister [7] **r**..... against my parents completely and went off to live in London when she was 17.

It isn't easy being a parent. My own kids are always [8] **p**..... me to buy them things that other children have, but I try not to [9] **g**..... in to these demands. Of course when they do something good, I might [10] **r**..... them with a present, but I don't want them to be spoilt!

7 **Dictation cultural differences in raising children**

2.37 Listen to a psychologist talking about raising children and complete the paragraphs. Which aspect of bringing up children do you sympathise most with?

Everything depends on .....
..... .

In other words, what .....
.....
..... ?

Do you want them .....
..... ?

If so, ...
.....
..... .

Or do you want them to be successful individuals? If so, ...
.....
..... .

Or is it important that they are good family members? Then .....
.....
..... .

10b Globalisation of the food market

Reading global food

1 Read the article. Who has the globalisation of food brought benefits for?
- a Everyone from the UK to Kenya.
- b People in developing countries in particular.
- c The richer people in the world, but not those in under-developed countries.

2 Read the article again and answer the questions.

1 The author thinks that the weekly family menu in Britain 50 years ago:
- a was very boring for those who had to eat it.
- b used food resources carefully.
- c was not very nutritious.

2 The main difference with a weekly family menu in Britain these days is that:
- a people don't plan what they are going to eat.
- b people have more money to eat out.
- c there is a greater choice of food.

3 The phrase 'homogenisation of taste' means:
- a we all eat similar things.
- b everything tastes more and more the same.
- c each type of food doesn't taste as strong as it did in the past.

4 The main reason that the price of food has increased globally is:
- a people in developing countries want more western-style food.
- b climate change has badly affected food production.
- c the general economic depression.

5 Higher food prices have caused people in the West to:
- a eat less meat.
- b not eat in restaurants.
- c economise on the food they eat.

GLOBALISATION OF THE FOOD MARKET

Globalisation has had a huge impact on eating habits all over the world. From the UK to Kenya to China, the food we eat today is determined by global markets and world economic events.

If you go back 50 years, a typical working family in Britain ate the same things every week – not that anyone complained about it. The weekly menu was built around the Sunday roast, when a large piece of meat – beef or lamb, for example – was served up with seasonal vegetables as a treat. On the following days, people used to eat leftovers from this 'feast' in a way that clearly avoided waste. On Monday they would have cold cuts of meat and on Tuesday a dish made from the remains, such as shepherd's pie. Wednesday and Thursday were less predictable, but Friday was 'Fish and Chips' day. Saturday was usually sausage and mash because this was quick and easy, and then it was back to the Sunday roast again.

Look at today's average weekly family menu in Britain and there is no comparison. For a start, there is no average: the element of predictability has disappeared, because what is on offer now is not just British but international cuisine. Chinese stirfry on Sunday, Italian lasagne on Wednesday, Mexican tortillas on Thursday. Secondly, seasonality is no longer a factor. If I want strawberries in December or asparagus in March, I can buy them, because even if it's not the season to grow them in the UK, it is in South Africa or Chile. Eating out is not the exceptional treat it used to be. It's fairly normal to eat out at least once a week and to have a takeaway – perhaps a curry – when you can't be bothered to cook.

But while globalisation may have brought more variety to our table, at the same time global food brands have brought a homogenisation of taste, particularly in snack foods and fast foods. You can buy a Kit Kat anywhere from Berne to Beijing, and no one is surprised any more when they see MacDonald's in some provincial town far from the USA.

This demand for Western foods, such as hamburgers and pizza, in countries where there is rapid economic development has had a dramatic effect on the price of wheat and other basic food commodities. Add to this crop failures from unfavourable weather conditions and the result is that we are all paying more for our food. In the West, this may cause us some inconvenience: eating chicken, which is less expensive, instead of beef for example, or cutting back on the number of times we eat out, but in under-developed countries the effect has been devastating. For a poor family in Kenya who are used to a diet of corn, rice and beans with meat maybe once or twice a week, the choice is not between goat or chicken, but rather rice with beans or rice without beans.

Glossary
treat (n) /triːt/ something special to reward people
mash (n) /mæʃ/ mashed potatoes

Grammar *used to, usually, be used to* and *get used to*

3 Choose the correct option according to the facts in the article.

1 Families in Britain *usually eat / were used to eating / used to eat* the same thing every week.
2 British families *were used to using / got used to using / used to use* the Sunday roast to make meals for the next two days.
3 Today people in Britain *are used to eating / get used to eating / used to eat* a variety of international foods.
4 They *usually eat / have got used to eating / used to be eat* whatever they want, whether it is in season or not.
5 They *usually eat out / got used to eating out / used to eat out* at least once a week.
6 People *usually see / are used to seeing / got used to seeing* MacDonald's everywhere in the world
7 People in Kenya *are used to eating / have got used to eating / used to eat* rice, corn, beans and a little meat.
8 Nowadays, in tougher times, they *usually eat / are used to eating / got used to eating* just beans and rice.

4 Read about an English person living 100 years ago. Which of the underlined verbs can be replaced with *used to, would* or *was/were used to*? Write the alternative.

'We [1] didn't cook on a stove, because we didn't have one. We [2] cooked everything over a fire. For example, if we [3] wanted to cook sausages, we [4] hung them on hooks over the fire. But if it [5] was a special occasion and we had a lot of things to cook, then we had to take it down the road to the hotel which [6] had a proper oven and for a few pennies they [7] cooked it for us. It seems strange now, but we [8] did that whenever all the family got round the table.'

1 *didn't use to cook* ..... 5 .....
2 ..... 6 .....
3 ..... 7 .....
4 ..... 8 .....

5 Pronunciation /uː/ and /juː/

a 2.38 Listen to the words. Write the words in the table.

blue consume fortune humanity humour lunar menu rude suit truce used usually

/uː/	/juː/
.....	.....
.....	.....
.....	.....
.....	.....
.....	.....
.....	.....

b 2.39 Now listen and check.

Vocabulary food types

6 Look at what these people ate for lunch. Which of the following did they have? Write staple food (S), dairy product (D), processed food (P) and fresh fruit and vegetables (F).

1 **Simon**
cheese sandwich .....
packet of crisps .....

2 **Kerry**
mixed salad .....
grapes .....
can of cola .....

3 **Will**
rice and stir-fried vegetables .....
instant coffee with milk .....

4 **Katie**
hamburger and chips .....
strawberry milkshake .....

10c Body language

Listening Desmond Morris

1 2.40 Listen to a description of the work of Desmond Morris. Are the sentences true (T) or false (F)?

1 Desmond Morris studied as a zoologist and a psychologist.
2 More than 90% of human communication is made using speech.
3 The first example describes the body language of Desmond Morris and a radio presenter.
4 Postural echo involves imitating someone's facial expressions.
5 In the second situation, it would be right to use postural echo.
6 Leaning back in your chair shows that you feel in control.

2 2.40 Look at the diagrams and answer the questions. Then listen again and check.

1 In the first situation, how are Desmond Morris and the presenter sitting? Choose the correct diagram.
2 How should the boss and the interviewee be sitting? Choose the correct diagram.

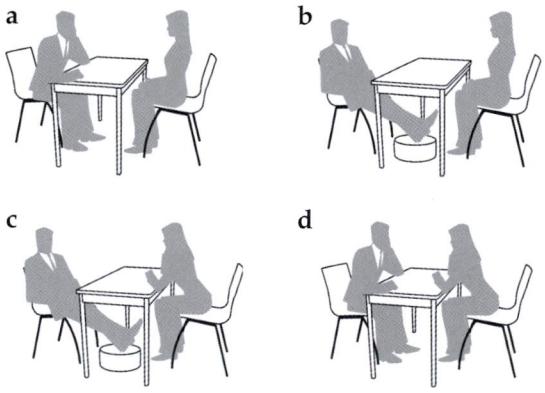

3 2.40 Choose the correct option to complete the sentences. Then listen again and check.

1 Morris's lifelong interest has been human *more/rather* than animal behaviour.
2 *Unlike/As* the traditional experts in human behaviour, he is not so interested in what people say, but rather in what they do.
3 In fact, he gives *few/little* attention to human speech.
4 In another situation, though, *that/such* postural echo might be inappropriate.
5 *The worst/At worst*, the boss would find it deeply insulting.

4 Pronunciation **unstressed syllables**

2.41 Look at these words. In each word, the second syllable is unstressed and contains the schwa /ə/ sound. Listen and repeat.

action	common	forward	human	little
other	posture	rather	student	verbal

Word focus *common*

5 Look at the two expressions in bold in the sentence below. Match the expressions with the correct definition (a or b).

It may be in the **common interest** of both the foreign and the national company to build a dam here, but I am not sure it is for the **common good**.

a something which benefits the public
.....
b something which benefits those involved
.....

6 Complete the crossword with expressions with *common*.

Across

4 an area where both parties agree: *common* …
5 something we should all possess: *common* …

Down

1 things that we all know: *common* …
2 things that we all make: *common* …
3 something that both parties benefit from: *common* …
4 something that benefits everyone: *common* …

				1 K			
2 M						3 I	
		4 G					
5 S							

10d Wedding customs

Vocabulary weddings

1 Write the words for these definitions.

1 a post-wedding holiday .....
2 promises the couple make to each other .....
3 a pre-wedding party for men only is a '..... night'
4 a covering for the bride's face .....
5 what you hear when a wedding is approaching .....
6 the man on his wedding day .....
7 an offer of marriage .....

Real life describing traditions

2 2.42 Listen to the description of the custom of dowry-giving and answer the questions.

1 What is a big dowry a sign of?
.....
2 What did the dowry act as compensation for?
.....
3 Which family normally gives the dowry?
.....
4 Which family gives the dowry in Nigeria?
.....
5 What do the guests at a Nigerian engagement party do, as well as dancing and having fun?
.....
6 What two things does a Nigerian dowry consist of?
.....

3 2.42 Complete the sentences with the words in the box. Then listen again and check.

customary marks occasion on place
rule symbolises traditional

1 Dowry-giving ..... different things, for example, a sign of wealth.
2 As a ....., in the past, brides did not go out to work.
3 It's ..... for a dowry to be given by the bride's family.
4 The engagement ceremony in Nigeria ..... the beginning of the wedding celebrations.
5 The ceremony is an ..... for people to have fun.
6 It takes ..... on the evening or a couple of nights before the wedding itself.
7 It used to be ..... for money to be thrown at the couple's feet.
8 ..... the night of the wedding, the bride goes back to her own house.

4 **Pronunication the letter *s***

2.43 Look at these words. Is the 's' sound /s/ or /z/? Listen and check.

		/s/	/z/			/s/	/z/
1	things	☐	☐	7	suit	☐	☐
2	house	☐	☐	8	kiss	☐	☐
3	brides	☐	☐	9	delivers	☐	☐
4	social	☐	☐	10	increase	☐	☐
5	sign	☐	☐	11	realise	☐	☐
6	clothes	☐	☐	12	is	☐	☐

5 **Listen and respond describing traditions**

2.44 Listen to some questions about wedding traditions and customs. Respond with your own words. Then compare your response with the model answer that follows.

1 *What does the groom wear on his wedding day?*

It's traditional for the groom to wear a morning suit and a top hat, but these days, he can also wear an ordinary suit.

10e Cultural differences

1 Writing skill elision in informal writing

Read the formal email (1) and the informal version (2). There are 16 differences. Find and underline as many as you can.

1

Dear Annabelle

It was very good to see you the other day. I hope you had a safe journey back to Leipzig. I forgot to mention that I am travelling to Poland next month on business to visit a supplier. I am unfamiliar with business customs in Poland and wondered if there was anything that I ought to be particularly aware of. For example, should I take some gifts with me? Will they be offended that I do not speak any Polish? I certainly do not want to offend my hosts in any way.

I do not want to inconvenience you, but if you have a moment to write a few words of advice, I would be most grateful.

With kind regards
Paul

2

Hi Annabelle

Very good to see you the other day. Hope you got back to Leipzig safely. I forgot to mention that I'm travelling to Poland next month on business to visit a supplier. I've really got no idea about business customs in Poland and wondered if there was anything I should know especially. For example, should I take some gifts with me? Will they be put out that I don't speak any Polish? I certainly don't want to put my foot in it with my hosts in any way.

I don't want to bother you, but if you've got a moment to write a few words of advice, I'd be really grateful.

All the best
Paul

Writing an informal email

2 Look at Annabelle's reply. Rewrite the underlined words and phrases so that they are in a more informal style.

[1] Dear Paul

[2] I enjoyed seeing you also and [3] thank you very much for [4] assisting me with my English CV. [5] I regret to say I don't know very much about Polish business customs but [6] here is a little advice.

A small gift – a souvenir of England perhaps – would be appreciated, I think. But [7] do not give them anything too [8] substantial as that would [9] cause embarrassment for them. [10] You will find that Polish business people [11] appear to be quite formal at a first meeting. [12] That is perfectly normal. Just spend time getting to know them and I [13] have no doubt that [14] they will relax. [15] Regarding the language, 'Milo mi' means [16] 'It is nice to meet you' and 'Dziekuje' means 'Thank you'.

[17] I hope it all goes well. Do [18] inform me about it [19] on your return.

[20] Yours sincerely

Annabelle

1	.....	11	.....
2	.....	12	.....
3	.....	13	.....
4	.....	14	.....
5	.....	15	.....
6	.....	16	.....
7	.....	17	.....
8	.....	18	.....
9	.....	19	.....
10	.....	20	.....

Wordbuilding word pairs

1 Make matching pairs. Match the words in box A with their 'partners' in box B.

A bride husband friends suit food
singing bits time plans pomp*
fun life

Glossary
***pomp** (n) /pɒmp/ magnificent display

B arrangements dancing drink ceremony
family games groom pieces soul
tie trouble wife

2 Complete the sentences with matching pairs from Exercise 1.

1 We wanted a simple wedding, without the ..... of a normal wedding.
2 Planning the wedding took ages, but it was worth all the ..... .
3 There's so much to organise at a wedding, including all the ..... that you never think about beforehand.
4 I'm so glad we invited James – he's always the ..... of the party.
5 It was a small wedding. We just invited a few ..... .
6 The woman usually wears a white dress and the man wears a ..... .

Learning skills making full use of your teacher

3 Use your teacher as a resource. Read these tips to help improve your English.

1 Pay attention to the way your teacher pronounces words and phrases and try to imitate them.
2 Every teacher uses certain idiomatic phrases and expressions. Ask them what they mean.
3 Ask the teacher to correct your mistakes, particularly your pronunciation. Even teachers can feel shy about doing this.
4 Ask your teacher what they think your main fault in English is and how you can correct it.
5 Tell your teacher what kinds of books you like to read and ask them to recommend some in English.
6 Make sure that you have the vocabulary you need (e.g. to describe your job). Ask your teacher to supply these words.

4 Answer these questions. Then check with your teacher. Does your teacher agree with you?

1 Can you pronounce these words from Unit 10?
  a disobey
  b dairy
  c future
2 Which one of these do you think you have most difficulty with?
  a using the right tense
  b lack of vocabulary
  c pronouncing things correctly
3 What can you do well in English?
  a study
  b communicate at work
  c get around in a foreign country

Check!

5 Complete these phrasal verbs and idiomatic phrases. You can find all the answers in Student's Book Unit 10.

Quiz Time

1 Try not to give ..... to all your children's demands. (preposition)
2 We don't eat ..... much these days because restaurants are so expensive. (preposition)
3 Parents who are very relaxed and laid-..... don't push their children to be high achievers. (preposition)
4 Sarah and I have a lot ..... common. (preposition)
5 Bringing up children is complicated, but if you use your common ..... you won't go far wrong. (noun)
6 We didn't agree at first, but in the end we found some common ..... . (noun)
7 Can you tell me what I should take as a present? I don't want to put my ..... in it. (noun)
8 In the UK, the party that a bride has with her friends before the wedding is called a ..... night. (noun)

Unit 11 Knowledge and learning

11a Conserving languages

Listening enduring voices

1 3.1 Listen to a description of the work of Dr K. David Harrison and the 'Enduring Voices' team at *National Geographic*. Which sentence (a–c) best summarises their work?

a to help different people in the world to communicate with each other
b to increase the number of languages spoken in the world
c to save dying languages from extinction

2 3.1 Read the questions. Then listen again and choose the best option (a–c).

1 How many languages will there be in the world in 2050?
a about 7,000
b about 3,500
c about 700

2 Bolivia is used as an example of a country with many languages because … .
a they are so different
b it has a large population
c it has as many languages as Europe

3 Yuchi is a language spoken in Oklahoma which … .
a has only 70 speakers
b is a dead language
c people are trying to revive

4 According to Dr Harrison, when we lose a language, we lose a culture's … .
a knowledge of the world
b important monuments
c stories

5 Speakers of Yupik have helped us to understand better … .
a the geography of the Arctic
b their language and culture
c the effects of climate change

6 The speaker thinks that globalisation highlights the importance of … .
a diversity
b finding common interests
c saving dying languages

3 3.1 Complete the sentences from the description using the correct form of these verbs. Then listen again and check.

document express record save seek out
store trace

1 He is part of a *National Geographic* project called 'Enduring Voices' whose aim is to ..... languages which are little known.
2 The race is on to ..... and ..... these languages.
3 Dr Harrison ..... these language 'hotspots'.
4 All cultures ..... their genius through their languages and stories.
5 These languages ..... knowledge which can be of huge benefit to people today.
6 Dr Harrison and his team aim to ..... as many languages as they can.

Grammar *could, was able to, manage to* and *succeed in*

4 Look at these sentences from the description. Choose the correct option.

1 Studies in the Oklahoma region of the USA *could discover / succeeded in discovering* 26 languages.
2 By highlighting this fact, researchers *could help / were able to help* the community to keep this dying language alive.
3 Some ancient cultures *could build / managed to build* large monuments by which we can remember their achievements.
4 A book written a few years ago by Yupik elders and scientists *was able to help / managed to help* other scientists to understand how climate change is affecting the polar ice.
5 One of the original arguments for globalisation was that it *could bring / managed to bring* us all closer together.
6 He *could save / couldn't save* Ubykh – a language spoken near the Black Sea – from extinction.

5 Complete the sentences about learning a language using *could, was/were able to, manage to* or *succeed in* and the verb in brackets. Sometimes more than one answer is possible.

1 The video I got was in Turkish, but I ..... (find) English subtitles on the main menu.
2 My sister is an amazing linguist: she ..... (speak) four languages fluently by the time she was twelve.
3 Esperanto was invented to be a world language, but supporters of it ..... (never / convince) enough people to use it.
4 When I first moved to England, I ..... (not / understand) native speakers because they seemed to mumble when they spoke.
5 I had a friend who was brought up speaking three different languages, but I was never sure if he ..... (express) himself clearly in any of them!
6 I spent eight years learning Italian, but when I tried to use it a couple of years ago, I found that I ..... (remember) the grammar but not the vocabulary.

Vocabulary learning

6 Match the expressions (1–8) with the correct definition (a–h).

1	pick up	a	become involved in
2	take in	b	not know about
3	learn by trial and error	c	learn as you go along
4	inspire	d	understand simply
5	have a basic grasp of	e	know about
6	engage with	f	absorb
7	be ignorant	g	motivate
8	be aware of	h	learn by making mistakes

7 Complete the sentences using a verb or expression from Exercise 6.

1 Don't worry about explaining. I'm sure I'll ..... it .....
2 She's a great teacher. She really knows how to ..... her students.
3 I used to be completely ..... about art, so I went on an art appreciation course.
4 I ..... of car mechanics, but I couldn't repair an electronic fault.
5 Mathematics is a difficult subject for some people to ..... because it's so theoretical.
6 Sorry, that's too much information to ..... all at once. Can you go through it more slowly?

8 Dictation languages

a 3.2 Listen to someone talking about languages, place names and words. Write the words that they spell.

1 a ..... b .....
2 a ..... b .....
3 a ..... b .....
4 .....
5 .....

b 3.2 Listen again and match the words from Exercise 8a with the correct meaning:

a a very long word in English .....
b the name of a college in the USA .....
c a word for an animal in a Siberian language .....
d an extinct language from the USA .....
e a new language found in India .....

11b Memory loss

Reading memory loss

1 Read the description of three types of memory loss quickly. Match the descriptions (1–3) with the summaries (a–c).

a When you can't recognise someone you know .....

b When your mind chooses to forget something it doesn't want to remember .....

c When you deceive yourself with a false memory .....

2 Read the descriptions again. Are the sentences true (T) or false (F)? Or is there not enough information (N) to say if the statements are true or false?

1 Lacunar amnesia is when people have had a bad shock and don't remember what happened.

2 In these cases, the memory is erased from the mind.

3 Sarah only remembers the moment when the truck hit the house.

4 Prosopamnesia is a condition some people inherit from their parents.

5 Philippa was concerned that the man who approached her was William Child.

6 William Child was upset that she didn't recognise him.

7 In source amnesia, people intentionally change the source of the memory.

8 In Jon's profession it is common to meet people with this condition.

9 The woman wanted her neighbour to be punished for the crime.

1 Lacunar amnesia

This literally means a gap in the memory. People who suffer from lacunar amnesia fail to remember a very specific event. It usually occurs when a person has suffered a traumatic event and their mind chooses to blank this out. The memory is still there in fact, but our psychological defences stop us remembering the event to protect us from suffering further psychological trauma.

Sarah's story: 'When I was a child, something extraordinary happened at our house. My sister and I were just about to go to bed and I was downstairs saying goodnight to our parents. My sister was going to say goodnight to them too, but had gone to the kitchen to get a glass of water. At that moment, a truck ran into the ground floor of our house. I know that because my sister, who was unhurt, told me afterwards. All I remember was saying goodnight, then waking up in hospital.'

2 Prosopamnesia

Prosopamnesia is an inability to remember faces. It is something that many people have in a mild form, but in severe cases sufferers can forget the faces of even close friends or associates. People can be born with this syndrome or it can be acquired during their lives.

Philippa's story: 'I'm terrible at remembering faces. I recall being at a conference at Berkeley University in California and another academic came up and started chatting to me. I would have asked his name, but knowing my inability to remember faces I didn't in case he was someone I was supposed to know. Anyway, it turned out that we had a friend and colleague in common. "Oh yes, I know Wiliam Child," I said. "We collaborated on a research project last year. He came to dinner at my house many times. How do you know him?" "I am Willliam Child", the man replied.'

3 Source amnesia

Also called 'memory distrust syndrome', source amnesia occurs when a person is unable to recall the context in which they learnt about something. Subconsciously, they then attribute the fact to some other, usually reliable, source. This can happen when the real source is not reliable and the person very much wants to believe that the fact is true.

Jon's story: 'I work as a lawyer, and in my line of work I often come across people who have persuaded themselves of a version of events that may not be true. I had a witness who was going to give evidence in court that her neighbour had thrown a brick at her car. She clearly believed that this had happened, and was determined that her neighbour wouldn't get away with it. But it turned out that it was not her own memory of events, but what another neighbour had told her.'

3 Find phrasal verbs in the text on page 86 with the following meanings:

1 erase (especially a memory) (para 1) .....
2 collided with (para 2) .....
3 approached (para 4) .....
4 was found (para 4) .....
5 find something (without expecting to) (para 6) .....
6 escape without punishment (para 6) .....

Grammar future in the past

4 There are six examples of the 'future in the past' forms in the text on page 86. Underline the examples. Which of the other future in the past forms could be used in each case?

was/were about to do	was/were going to	
was supposed to	would do	would have done

1 *My sister and I were just about to go to bed … or were just going to go to bed …*
2 .....
3 .....
4 .....
5 .....
6 .....

5 Complete the sentences using a future in the past form. Sometimes more than one form is possible.

1 'I'm so sorry. I ..... (write) you a letter, but I lost your address.'
2 'I ..... (just / book) tickets to visit Munich, but then I remembered that it was Oktoberfest and all the hotels ..... (be) full.'
3 'I promised her I ..... (speak) to my boss about finding her a job, but I forgot.'
4 'The meeting ..... (last) only an hour, but just as we ..... (finish), Julian remembered that we hadn't discussed the move to our new offices.'
5 'I ..... (take) my driving test sooner, but I didn't feel ready.'
6 'That's funny. I ..... (just / ask) you exactly the same question.'

6 Pronunciation contrastive sentence stress

a 3.3 Underline the words in the first half of the sentences that are most strongly stressed. Then listen and check.

1 I was going to email him, but I decided it would better to speak face to face.
2 He was supposed to get here early, but he's already ten minutes late.
3 I would have come by train, but there's a strike on at the moment.
4 She said she would be pleased if I talked to him, but she seemed really angry.
5 I was about to buy a flat, but Katie said I could rent hers for six months while she was away.
6 Liz was going to be in charge of the project, but now she's just acting as an advisor.

b 3.3 Underline the words in the second half of the sentences that are most strongly stressed. Practise saying each sentence. Then listen again and check.

7 Grammar extra future phrases

FUTURE PHRASES

Notice that we use other phrases with the infinitive to talk about the future.
*She's **bound to** want to leave early.*
*He's **likely to** change his mind.*
*You're **unlikely to** find the information here.*

Look at the grammar box. Then look at phrases (1–5) which talk about the future. Match the phrases to the correct definition (a–e).

1 I'm sorry, but I always thought it was a terrible idea. It was **bound to** fail.
2 The plane was **due to** take off at 7 a.m., but poor weather meant it was delayed.
3 We thought that it was **unlikely** to be cold, so we didn't take any warm clothes with us.
4 It was **about to** rain so we decided to eat inside.
5 The political situation was **likely** to get worse, so we left the country for our own safety.

a not probable
b probable
c certain
d scheduled / expected
e on the point of

11c Intelligent animals

Listening

1 Match the name of the animal with the correct picture.

Bonobo monkey border collie crow
dolphin scrub-jay

1 .....

2 .....

3 .....

4 .....

5 .....

2 3.4 Listen to a description of five intelligent animals. Write the number of the description (1–5) next to the intelligent behaviour that this type of animal is known for.

a They are good at copying what they see. ☐
b They are good at communicating. ☐
c They like to follow instructions. ☐
d They make plans for the future. ☐
e They make implements to get different jobs done. ☐

3 3.4 Listen again and write the number of the description next to the intelligent action each animal did.

a found a clever way to reach some food ☐
b did acrobatics in time with one another ☐
c made food disappear ☐
d learned to match a two-dimensional image to a real object ☐
e cooked himself a treat ☐

4 Match the words from the descriptions with the adjectives below (1–5).

inventive mischievous smart expressive playful

1 intelligent .....
2 creative .....
3 fun-loving .....
4 communicative .....
5 naughty .....

Word focus *learn*

5 Complete the sentences using expressions with *learn*.

1 You have to learn to w..... before you can run.
2 It's never too l..... to learn.
3 In life, you have to learn from your m.....
4 I learnt a few t..... of the trade.
5 Never again. I've learnt my l.....
6 Just learn to l..... with it!
7 I learnt the hard w.....
8 I've learnt the whole poem by h.....

11d Ask the teacher

Real life getting clarification

1 Complete these phrases with the correct verb.

1 What do you ..... by 'difficult'?
2 Can you ..... up a little? I can't hear you.
3 Can you ..... what the exam at the end of the course involves?
4 I'm sorry. I ..... not really with you.
5 Are you ..... that learning the historical dates isn't important?
6 Could you ..... me an example of an important historian of the last century?
7 There's a lot of information to ..... in.
8 I didn't ..... that last word. Can you repeat it?

2 3.5 Listen to a conversation between a student and a college lecturer. Answer the questions.

1 What is the course?
.....
.....
2 What is the student worried about?
.....
.....
3 What does the lecturer recommend?
.....
.....

3 3.5 Listen again and complete the student's questions.

1 Can you explain .....
.....?
2 And are you saying that .....
.....?
3 Sorry, I'm not really with you. You mean
.....?
4 Could you give me an example of .....
.....?
5 Did you say .....
.....?

4 Grammar extra verbs with indirect objects

▶ VERBS WITH INDIRECT OBJECTS

Some verbs, e.g. *tell* and *show* can be followed by an indirect personal object. Other verbs, e.g. *say* and *explain*, don't always need an indirect personal object. If you use an indirect personal object with these verbs, you must put *to* before the object.

*He told **me** about the history course.*
*I showed **him** a copy of the lecture notes.*
*They explained (**to me**) that I could find the reading list online.*

Look at the sentences below and write the pronoun *me* where necessary.

1 Can you tell ..... how many hours of study we're expected to do each week?
2 Do you recommend ..... that I should read Stephen Hawking's book?
3 She said ..... that I could get most of the books from the library.
4 She also explained ..... that the library was open until 10 p.m.
5 Can you show ..... how that works?
6 He taught ..... that I didn't always need to write such long essays.

5 Pronunciation linking in question forms

3.6 Practise saying these sentences. Then listen and compare your pronunciation.

1 Did you say 'Africa'?
2 Could you explain that?
3 What do you mean by 'difficult'?
4 Can you give me an example?
5 What are you saying?

6 Listen and respond getting clarification

3.7 Listen to a conversation between a teacher and a student (you). Respond with your own words. Then compare your response with the model answer that follows.

1

So you wanted to ask me a question about the exam at the end of this course?

Yes. Can you explain what the exam involves?

11e A letter to a college

Writing an email about a misunderstanding

1 Match the two parts of the sentences about a misunderstanding over an application for a course. What seems to be the problem according to the writer?

1 The website said the deadline for entries was 20 August.
2 Despite the fact that my application arrived in time,
3 I am not someone who does things at the last minute.
4 While I appreciate that you have a lot of applicants for this course,
5 Whereas most colleges seem to select applicants on the merits of their application,

a you choose people on a 'first come, first served' basis.
b I cannot understand why you have chosen to ignore those people who applied after July.
c In fact, I sent in my application at the end of July.
d On the contrary, I am always careful to observe deadlines.
e I was told that I had missed the deadline.

2 Writing skill linking contrasting ideas

Rewrite these sentences from the reply to the applicant's letter using the words given.

1 We sympathise with your situation, but it is too late to do anything about it now. (while)

.....

.....

2 Despite the fact that you sent your form in before the deadline, we had already received too many applications. (although)

.....

.....

3 You say in your letter that we have no right to do this, but the college has the right to close the application process early. (in actual fact)

.....

.....

4 We are very careful to follow the rules. We don't 'make up the rules as we go along' as you suggest. (on the contrary)

.....

.....

5 Most colleges would keep your application fee, but we are refunding it to you. (whereas)

.....

.....

3 Look at the notes and write a letter to a college. Include the following points.

a Reason for writing: you can't attend the accountancy course this term.
b Misunderstanding: you thought it was an evening class, but it's during the day.
c Effort on your part: your company would like to give you time off, but they can't.
d Apology: probably your mistake, but these things happen.
e Action required: want the college to refund the money paid for the course fee.

Dear Sir / Madam

a .....
.....
.....

b .....
.....
.....

c .....
.....
.....

d .....
.....
.....

e .....
.....
.....

I look forward to .....
.....

Yours .....

Wordbuilding idiomatic expressions

1 Read the story. What do the idiomatic expressions in bold (1–6) mean? Match the idiomatic expressions with the definitions (a–f).

> I don't know when [1] **it first dawned on me** that it would be a good idea to grow my own vegetables. I know [2] **it struck me** some time ago that vegetables in the shops were getting very expensive. [3] **It occurred to me** that if more people grew their own, we wouldn't have to import so many. I [4] **didn't have a clue** about growing plants, but then I read a fantastic book written by woman called Joy Larkcom. The book really [5] **opened my eyes.** That was six years ago and it has become more than a hobby. [6] **It never crossed my mind** that I would become an expert, but now a lot of neighbours come and ask me for my advice.

a I had a strong impression .....
b helped me to see the truth .....
c was ignorant .....
d I realised .....
e I had the idea .....
f I didn't ever think .....

Learning skills techniques for memorising

2 People remember things in different ways. Some remember better by hearing (auditory learners), some by seeing (visual learners) and some by doing or by action (kinaesthetic learners). It is important to know how you remember things. What do you remember of the following items in Unit 11?

1 Maria Fadiman's work on conservation of plants. .....
2 How *could* is different from *managed to*.
.....
3 The intelligence of Alex, the grey parrot.
.....
4 Useful phrases for checking understanding.
.....
5 Idiomatic expressions containing the word *learn*. .....

3 How did you remember the information? Was it through something:
a you heard?
b you saw?
c you did?

4 Look at these tips for memorising. Tick (✓) the one(s) you feel suit you best.

a **Auditory**: Record five words that you need to learn, giving each a translation or putting them into a sentence. Then listen to them again last thing at night.
b **Visual**: Draw a picture of the words that you need to learn. Look at the pictures the following day and see if you can remember the words.
c **Kinesthetic**: Work with another student and simulate a situation that illustrates the meaning of the word. Or think of an action that would help you remember the word.

5 Try to memorise these words and expressions from Unit 11 using the tips in Exercise 4.

absorb grasp gut feeling learn your lesson a misunderstanding

Check!

6 Complete the crossword.

Across
1 Maria Fadiman's stories help students to ..... with the subject (6)
5 a ..... memory remembers only what it wants (9)
7 another word for advice (8)
8 the opposite of your 'internal' memory (8)
10 'Sorry I didn't ..... your name.' (5)

Down
2 if you understand something in a simple way, you have 'a basic .....' of it (5)
3 you can *manage to do* or ..... *in doing* something (7)
4 a person who studies plants (8)
6 the opposite of knowing is being ..... (8)
8 one way of learning is by trial and ..... (5)
9 'It's never too ..... to learn.'

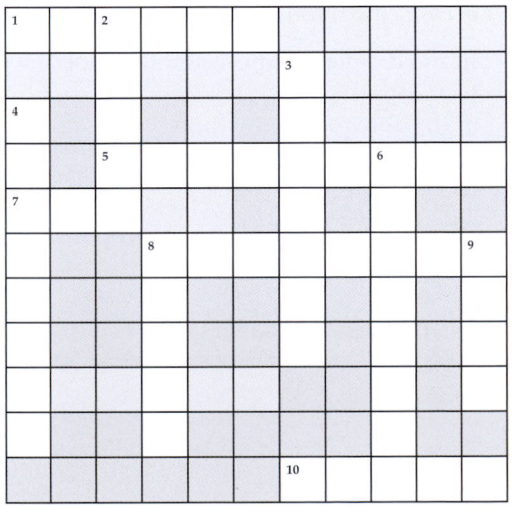

Unit 12 The economy

12a Economics

Listening character and economics

1 3.8 Listen to an economist giving his opinion about how character affects economics. Answer the questions.

1 Concerning attitudes to money, what two types of people does the economist describe?

.....

2 Can we apply these stereotypes to particular countries? Why? / Why not?

.....

.....

2 3.8 Listen again and choose the best option (a–c) to complete the sentences.

1 People who are prudent spend money … .
   a when they see something they really want
   b when it's for something of lasting benefit
   c on what's necessary

2 People who are extravagant with money say that they want to … .
   a enjoy life while they can
   b save but can't
   c increase their possessions

3 Some commentators said that certain countries who had borrowed money … .
   a hadn't worked hard enough
   b hadn't paid enough tax
   c hadn't been careful with the money

4 A lender faces the possibility of losing money and … .
   a creating problems for the borrower
   b going out of business
   c waiting a long time for payment

5 In most developed economies people want to … .
   a be able to borrow money
   b live more comfortably
   c reduce their debts

6 We need … to behave more responsibly.
   a spenders
   b savers
   c spenders and savers

3 Match the words in box A with a synonym in box B.

A fund prudent transaction wages wasteful

B careful deal extravagant finance salaries

Vocabulary rich and poor

4 Find and circle the words in the word search that mean the following:

1 poor
2 have enough money
3 inexpensive (2 words)
4 expensive
5 income
6 comfortable
7 very rich

R	H	P	I	M	O	I	N
E	A	R	N	I	N	G	S
A	R	I	C	C	F	O	T
S	D	C	H	E	A	P	O
O	U	E	S	O	F	U	L
N	P	Y	B	A	F	L	E
A	W	E	L	L	O	F	F
B	I	L	E	F	R	A	T
L	O	A	D	E	D	E	S
E	S	T	O	N	R	I	A

Grammar focus adverbs *only, just, even, too, as well, also*

5 Complete the sentences with these adverbs. Sometimes more than one adverb is possible.

also as well even just only too

1 Let's ..... consider people's attitude to money at its simplest level.
2 Of course, savers spend money ....., but ..... when they can afford it.
3 People in these countries would have to work longer hours, pay more taxes and ..... accept lower wages.
4 You risk losing the money but you ..... risk putting the borrower in a difficult situation.
5 We need both types of person, but ..... if they lend and borrow responsibly.

6 Write the focus adverbs in the correct place in the sentences.

1 Some people believe that if you go through life saving money, you will never have any fun. ONLY
2 Some people carry on spending money when they can't afford to. EVEN
3 You can guard against bad times by putting aside a small amount of money each week. JUST
4 If a few people save money, the banks won't have any to lend. ONLY
5 I'm not the only person who has debts. Other people have them. ALSO
6 Attitude to money is partly a cultural thing, but it has something to do with your upbringing. AS WELL
7 Some people are careful with money in hard times and in good times. TOO
8 Borrowers admit that they sometimes borrow money irresponsibly. EVEN

Vocabulary money

7 Complete these sentences with the correct noun. Use the verbs in brackets to help you.

1 To buy the car, I had to make ..... of £70 a month for five years. (pay)
2 We need to cut back on our ..... because the cost of living has become so high. (spend)
3 They say that gold is a good ..... at the moment. (invest)
4 We took out a ..... from the bank to finance the purchase of our apartment. (lend)
5 If you can't afford university fees, then the government gives you a ..... . (give)
6 We wanted to increase our ..... so that we could build an extension on our house. (borrow)
7 The public ..... of the USA are counted in trillions of dollars rather than billions. (owe)
8 Public sector workers are protesting because their ..... have been frozen for the last two years. (earn)

8 **Dictation money and lifestyle**

3.9 Listen to someone talking about money and lifestyle, and write down the words you hear.

I think that .....

.....

.....

It's a lifestyle .....

.....

.....

.....

This desire .....

.....

.....

.....

12b Cheap labour

Reading the slave economy

1 Read the article. What is the main message?
a Business does well from using cheap labour.
b All industries use cheap labour.
c The American economy has always relied on cheap labour.

2 Look back at the article. Are the sentences true (T) or false (F)? Or is there not enough information (N) to say if the sentences are true or false?

1 It is only in recent years that businesses have started moving to where labour is cheaper.
2 The colonists of the Americas needed a lot of labour to take economic advantage of their new territory.
3 Native Americans as well as African people were used as slaves.
4 The practice of slavery was quite common around the Mediterranean, even before the colonisation of America.
5 African slaves seemed to work harder than slaves from other regions.
6 The African slave population of the Americas outnumbered the Europeans by more than five to one.
7 The slaves in cities were treated better than those living on the plantations.
8 A kind of slavery – not paying people a fair amount of money for the work they do – still exists in the world today.

The history of successful industries has always been a story of cheap labour. Clearly, if you can get people to work for very little, your business will be more profitable. Even in more recent times, you can track the movement of industry – textiles and tuna canning are two striking examples – to the places where the work can be done more cheaply.

But imagine the profits if your labourers work for nothing. In other words, if you use slaves as the European colonial powers of the 16th to the 19th centuries did. Those countries which had colonised the Americas became dependent on enslaved labour for their survival. Colonial officials believed that the land they had 'discovered' in the Americas was useless without sufficient labour to exploit it. However, since there were not sufficient European or Native American workers, large numbers of African people were captured and transported to the Americas to work.

The trans-Saharan slave trade had long supplied slaves from central Africa to work on sugar plantations in the Mediterranean. Having proved themselves competent workers in Europe, enslaved Africans became the labour force of choice in colonial America.

Of the 6.5 million immigrants who survived the crossing of the Atlantic and settled in the western hemisphere between 1492 and 1776, only one million were Europeans. The remaining 5.5 million were African. 80 percent of these enslaved Africans were employed as field-workers. Women as well as children worked. Only the very young and infirm escaped. Their 'owners' put them to work first on the sugar plantations, then on tobacco plantations and, following the invention of the cotton gin in 1793, on cotton plantations. These products brought great riches to the United States.

Even though the majority of slaves were employed in agriculture, there were many in other jobs – as butlers, waiters, maids, carriage drivers, blacksmiths and stable boys. In urban areas, such as New Orleans and Philadelphia, where they accounted for up to a third of the population, their owners forced the slaves to learn the trades of carpenter, stonemason, baker, etc. And so not just agriculture, but the whole economy came to depend on this free labour. At the same time, the British textile industry grew rich making clothes from America's cheap imported cotton.

Unfortunately, even though slavery was abolished a long time ago, the temptation to exploit people for extra profit by employing them on low wages has not gone away.

Glossary
cotton gin (n) /ˈkɒt(ə)n dʒɪn/ a machine that separates cotton fibre from the seeds
plantation (n) /plænˈteɪʃ(ə)n/ a farm where a crop such as cotton is grown
stable boy (n) /ˈsteɪbl bɔɪ/ a boy who looks after horses

3 Find words or expressions in the article with the following meanings.

1 follow (para 1)
.....

2 making a strong impression (para 1)
.....

3 enough (para 2)
.....

4 good at one's job (para 3)
.....

5 favoured or preferred (para 3)
.....

6 weak, sick or disabled (para 4)
.....

7 someone who works with iron and metal (para 5)
.....

8 a skilled manual job (para 5)
.....

Grammar causative *have* and *get*

4 Put the words in brackets into the right form to complete these sentences.

1 It's evident that if you can ..... (have / people / work) for very little money, your business is going to be more profitable.

2 Companies are always searching for a country where they can ..... (get / their work / do) more cheaply.

3 Imagine how much more profitable it is if you ..... (get / your labourers / work) for nothing.

4 The traders who sent slaves to the Mediterranean also ..... (have / 10,000 slaves a year / send) to serve owners in America.

5 The slave 'owners' ..... (get / the slaves / work) first on the sugar plantations, then on tobacco plantations.

6 On the plantations, the owners ..... (have / their slaves / work) as butlers, waiters, maids, etc.

7 In urban areas, their owners ..... (get / them / learn) various trades.

8 In the 19th century, the British textile industry ..... (have / cheap cotton / ship) over from America.

5 Pronunciation the sounds /ʃ/, /tʃ/, /ʒ/ and /dʒ/

a 3.10 Listen to these words from the article and complete the table.

abolished carriage cheap decision
riches sugar usually wages

/ʃ/	/tʃ/	/ʒ/	/dʒ/
wash	watch	pleasure	change
.....	.....	.....	.....
.....	.....	.....	.....

b 3.11 Now listen and check.

Vocabulary domestic jobs

6 Complete the sentences about repairs to a house. The first letter of each verb has been given.

1 We need to get someone to f..... this carpet. The shape of the room is so irregular.

2 I've asked John to p..... up some new shelves in the living room. He's a professional carpenter.

3 I think we can d..... the room ourselves. We don't need to have it done by a professional painter.

4 The kitchen units came in pieces and I had to a..... them by myself. It took me about seven hours.

5 Can you call a roofer? The roof's still leaking and we need to get it f..... .

6 You know that guy who t..... our bathroom walls – he did a terrible job. There are cracks everywhere.

7 Do you know anyone who can p..... a ceiling? We have cracks in our living room and I'm worried the ceiling's going to come down.

8 Can you help me to h..... this picture on the wall?

7 Look at these DIY jobs and match each one with the professional who does it.

1 fixing a leaky tap	a a gardener
2 rewiring a house	b a plumber
3 cutting the grass	c a carpenter or joiner
4 demolishing a wall	d a general builder
5 fitting a new front door	e a decorator
6 painting the outside of a house	f an electrician

12c The world of barter

Listening an interview

1 3.12 Listen to an interview with a member of the Barter Society. What is the advantage of barter, according to him? Choose the correct option (a–c).

a You can exchange things without paying tax.
b It opens up a whole new world of people to do business with.
c You get a much better deal than you would if you used cash.

Glossary
GDP (n) /ˌdʒiːdiːˈpiː/ gross domestic product
spear (n) /spɪə/ a long, pointed weapon used in hunting
tree surgeon (n) /ˈtriː ˌsɜːdʒ(ə)n/ a specialist in cutting off damaged parts of trees

2 3.12 Listen again and choose the best option (a–c) to complete the sentences.

1 The example of barter given by the interviewer is an exchange of a chicken for:
a an item of clothing.
b some food.
c a weapon.

2 Barter is a system of trade that:
a all primitive societies use.
b is still used widely today.
c has always had a small group of followers.

3 'Exchange barter' is a system:
a that involves two people exchanging goods with one another.
b that involves being a member of a club of other barterers.
c where you exchange goods up to a certain value.

4 Barter exchanges:
a aren't taxed.
b are taxed if they are above a certain value.
c are taxed in some countries.

5 The advantage of direct barter groups is that they:
a mean you can reach a big group of potential customers.
b allow you to pay less tax.
c avoid currency exchange.

Word focus *hard*

3 Complete the text using an expression with *hard*. There are two extra expressions.

hard bargain	hard work	hard feelings	hard up
hard-headed	hard luck	hard done by	

If you are [1] _____ and short of cash, then barter may be a good solution for you. You don't have to be a [2] _____ business person to make it work, because exchanges are done in a spirit of co-operation. In direct barter, the negotiation is friendly and there is no question of trying to drive a [3] _____. So there are never any [4] _____ between the barterers, with one person feeling they have 'won' in the deal and the other feeling [5] _____.

4 Grammar extra ***hard* and *hardly***

▶ *HARD* and *HARDLY*

The adjective *hard* has two different adverb forms: *hard* and *hardly*.
I'm trying ***hard*** *to see the advantage of it.* (I'm making a big effort.)
It ***hardly*** *seems worth the effort.* (It's almost NOT worth the effort.)

Note the position of the *hard* and *hardly* in relation to the verb.

Look at the grammar box. Then complete the sentences using *hard* and *hardly* and the verbs in the correct form.

1 runs / hard
a He _____. He'll be very fit if he manages to keep it up.
b He _____. It's more of a walk.

2 works / hard
a She _____ now. She goes in to the office once a week, I think.
b She _____ now. She has a new boss who's very demanding.

3 know / hard
I _____ him. We've met twice, I think.

4 thought / hard
a I _____ about it. It wasn't an easy decision.
b I _____ about work when I was away on holiday.

5 tried / hard
a The team _____. It was as if they didn't care.
b The team _____, but they weren't good enough to win.

12d Organising an event

Real life negotiating

1 Match the expressions (1–6) with phrases with the same meaning (a–f).

1	to be honest	a	in your shoes
2	the key thing	b	what's important
3	let's face it	c	when all's said and done
4	if I were you	d	to tell you the truth
5	at the end of the day	e	you must understand
6	you have to appreciate	f	be realistic

2 3.13 Listen to two people in a negotiation and answer the questions.

1 What event are they discussing?

.....

.....

2 What does the client try to negotiate?

.....

.....

3 3.13 Complete the phrases from the negotiation. Then listen and check.

1 We want some food but, to be ....., nothing too fancy.
2 OK, so what did you have in ..... ? A few canapés, some sandwiches?
3 Well, I was ..... we could have something a bit more exciting than sandwiches.
4 Yes, that ..... be much more like it.
5 That's quite a lot, but let's ..... it, it is an important occasion.
6 If I were in your ....., I'd like to put on an event that people would remember.
7 You have to ..... that we have to come and set it all up and take it away anyway.
8 I see. Well, the ..... thing for us is that it's a nice relaxing event.

4 **Pronunciation** sentence stress in idiomatic phrases

3.14 Listen to these phrases used in a negotiation. Underline the words that are stressed. Then practise saying them.

1 Can I just explain our position?
2 To tell you the truth, …
3 If you look at it from our side, …
4 That's going to be a bit of a sticking point.
5 To be perfectly honest, …
6 What you have to bear in mind is …

5 **Grammar extra** *would*

> ▶ ***WOULD***
>
> The function of *would* is to make what you say sound more polite or diplomatic, so it is often used in negotiations.
> *Yes, that **would** be much more like it.*
> ***Would** that reduce the price a bit then?*

Rewrite these sentences using *would* to make the sentences more diplomatic.

1 I'm afraid that will be difficult for me.

.....

2 Can you move a bit on the price?

.....

3 Are you willing to negotiate?

.....

4 I need to have some kind of guarantee.

.....

5 When do you need to know?

.....

6 I don't want to put you to any trouble.

.....

6 **Listen and respond** negotiating

3.15 You are hiring a caterer to provide food at a party. Listen to what the caterer says and respond with your own words. Then compare your response with the model answer that follows.

1

So what kind of food did you have in mind? Some sandwiches?

I was hoping we could have some hot food too.

12e A proposal

1 Writing skill sub-headings and bullet points
Look at the first extract from a report. What is the report about?

.....

I have now spoken on the phone to two different caterers about the food to be served at the Annual General Meeting (AGM). One was Angel Foods, which is a local firm, and the other is Carrick's, a much bigger chain of caterers that do catering in London and other major cities all over the country.

Summary
Two caterers have been approached about food for the AGM:
- Angel Foods, a local firm
- Carrick's, a national catering chain

2 Rewrite these extracts from the rest of the report. Use bullet points and concise language.

1
There are several things that we ought to think about before we make a decision. How much food do we need to provide? How much is it going to cost us? Do people have any special dietary needs that we should take into consideration?

Three factors to consider
- .....
- .....
- .....

2
The caterer has suggested various types of food – some hot food which will cost about £10 per person (quite pricey, I think) and cold food which costs about £7 per person.

The caterer
- .....
- .....

3
I suggest that we should go with Angel Foods, because they seemed to understand better what we want, and I think they will do it all for a better price.

Recommendation
.....
.....

Writing a report

3 Read the report. Then rewrite it in the framework given, making the language more concise and using sub-headings and bullet points.

I met a caterer, Party foods Ltd., yesterday and we discussed the food and arrangements for our office party on 12th December and this was what they proposed. They suggested that we have a range of different types of sandwiches and also hot and cold canapés. Sandwiches on their own would cost £6 per person and a mixture of sandwiches and cold canapés would be £8 per person. If the canapés were hot this would be an extra £2 per person – so a total of £10 per person.

Also, if we want, they can provide drinks. Alternatively, we can buy our own and they will charge a small amount for serving them – I think she said an extra £1 per person.

I think we should go for the mixture of sandwiches and cold canapés, and then provide our own drinks. I'd be happy to organise that part of it.

Subject: Office party 12th December

Summary
.....
.....
.....

Food
- .....
- .....
- .....

Drinks
- .....
- .....

Recommendation
.....
.....

Wordbuilding *the* + adjective

1 Can you think of the right adjective for these groups of people in society?

1 People with a lot of money *the rich*
2 People without a job .....
3 People with very little money .....
4 People with nowhere to live .....
5 People over 70 .....
6 People who are well known .....
7 People who can't see .....
8 People who can't hear .....
9 People who can't read or write .....
10 People who are unwell .....

2 Which of the answers in Exercise 1 describe people in a positive situation (P), a negative situation (N), or neither positive or negative (X).

Learning skills using the internet

3 The following ideas are ways you could use the internet to help you learn. Tick (✓) the ideas you could use.

1 Listen to or watch the news in English, e.g. on the BBC website. Note down key words as you listen to each story. Check their meaning online or in a dictionary. Then listen again.
2 Search for articles relevant to your interests on newspaper websites. Read the title and the first paragraph. Either mentally or on paper, note down two questions you would like answered by the article. Then read the article and find the answers.
3 If you are not sure how to pronounce a word, check in an online dictionary. Then practise saying it.
4 If you listen to English or American songs, search for the lyrics online. Follow them as you listen to the song. Look up any words you don't know.
5 Search for interesting quotations, sayings and anecdotes on websites. Try to memorise them.

4 Use the internet to find the following:

1 What does the word 'spin' mean in the context of political news?
.....
2 How do you pronounce 'rhythm'?
.....
3 What are the opening lyrics to 'Big Yellow Taxi' by Joni Mitchell?
.....
4 A good quotation on the subject of 'success'.
.....

Check!

5 Complete the sentences about the economy using information from Unit 12. Then use the first letters of each word to make something that many of us dream of having!

1 Poverty is a ..... concept. You can be classified as poor if you earn less than 60% of the average person.
2 Norway is a country that has saved money for the future rather than ..... it all in its infrastructure.
3 The servant economy is growing in developed countries; even people who are not very well-off have a ..... come and tidy the house once a week.
4 In the Stone Age, ... gatherers had a kind of gift economy. This was because they had a lot and needed little.
5 'At the ..... of the day' is a commonly used phrase in negotiations.
6 The opposite of saving money is ..... it.

Word: .....

3.16

LISTENING TEST

SECTION 1

Questions 1–10

Questions 1–3

*Choose the correct letter, **A**, **B** or **C**.*

Example

How did Martin first hear about the careers day?
A his tutor made an announcement.
B he saw a notice advertising it.
C a friend told him about it.

1 The careers day will be held
A in the college where Martin studies.
B in a public building.
C in the open air.

2 How long does Martin plan to spend at the careers day?
A a couple of hours
B half the day
C the full day

3 The Careers Day Website is available
A to anyone who pays an additional fee.
B only to those enrolled at the college.
C for a limited period of time only.

Questions 4–5

Choose ***TWO*** letters ***A–E***.

Which two activities are available during the lunch break?

A advice on CV writing
B talks by previous graduates
C personal interviews with careers advisers
D group discussions with recruitment agencies
E video on opportunities to do voluntary work overseas

4 .....

5 .....

Questions 6–10

Complete the notes below.

Write ***NO MORE THAN TWO WORDS AND/OR A NUMBER*** *for each answer.*

CAREERS DAY Scheduled Talks			
Time	Faculty	Speaker	Topic
10.00	Law	Professor **6**	contracts of employment
11.00	**7**	Professor Smith	internships
12.00	Languages	Dr Sally Wentworth	**8** .....
13.00	Lunch break		
14.00	Engineering	Dr Shah	opportunities in the **9** .....
15.00	Sports Science	Professor Bellucci	Olympic Games
16.00	**10**	Dr Fulton	interview techniques

SECTION 2

Questions 11–20

Questions 11 and 12

*Choose the correct letter, **A**, **B** or **C**.*

11 If you visit Jodrell Bank, you can
- **A** walk close to the telescope.
- **B** go on a guided tour of the buildings.
- **C** meet the scientists who work on the site.

12 A family ticket in the winter costs
- **A** £19.50.
- **B** £20.
- **C** £25.

Questions 13 and 14

*Choose **TWO** letters **A–E**.*

Which two facilities are currently available at the visitor centre?

- **A** cinema
- **B** lecture theatre
- **C** interactive displays
- **D** refreshments
- **E** planetarium

13 .....

14 .....

Questions 15–20

Complete the table below.

*Write **NO MORE THAN TWO WORDS AND/OR A NUMBER** for each answer.*

History of Jodrell Bank	
Year	Event
1939	The site was purchased by the university's **15** ..... department.
1945	Bernard Lovell moved some radar equipment to the site. Installation coincided with a **16** ....., which Lovell observed.
17	Giant Transit telescope built at Jodrell Bank.
1957	The telescope was replaced by one originally called the **18** ..... telescope.
1972	Arboretum created featuring a scale model of the **19** .....
2011	New visitor centre opened. Jodrell Bank proposed as a possible **20** ..... site.

SECTION 3

Questions 21–30

Questions 21–24

Choose the correct letter, ***A****,* ***B*** *or* ***C****.*

21 When asked if the elective is like a holiday, Damian
- **A** suggests that this depends on the individual.
- **B** admits that he spent too much time enjoying himself.
- **C** denies that his placement was unusual in this respect.

22 Why did Damian find it hard to organise his elective?
- **A** He had never travelled alone.
- **B** He was unfamiliar with other cultures.
- **C** He wasn't sure what he wanted to specialise in.

23 How does Damian feel about splitting his elective between two places?
- **A** He wishes he hadn't decided to do that.
- **B** He thinks he spent too long in one place.
- **C** He insists that he made the right decision.

24 When choosing a company to help him find an elective placement, Damian
- **A** relied on word-of-mouth recommendations.
- **B** did thorough research on the Internet.
- **C** tried not to be influenced by price.

Questions 25 and 26

Complete the sentences below.

Write ***NO MORE THAN TWO WORDS*** *for each answer.*

Damian decided to look for an elective placement specialising in **25** ..... medicine.

Damian chose Belize because he was impressed by pictures of the **26** ..... there.

Questions 27–30

Complete the notes below.

Write ***NO MORE THAN THREE WORDS*** *for each answer.*

BELIZE

Total Population: **27** .....

Area where Damian worked: **28** .....

Nationality of most doctors: **29** .....

What Damian would do if he returned to Belize: **30** .....

SECTION 4

Questions 31–35

Complete the notes below.

Write ***NO MORE THAN THREE WORDS*** *for each answer.*

Antiguan Racer Snake	
Length:	**31** .....
Colouring of male:	**32** .....
Colouring of female:	**33** .....
Preferred habitat:	**34** .....
Diet:	**35** .....

Questions 36–38

Complete the sentences below.

Write ***NO MORE THAN TWO WORDS*** *for each answer.*

Until 1995, the snake was thought to be extinct.

In 1995 it was rediscovered living on **36** ..... island.

A **37** ..... was commissioned by the Antiguan Forestry Unit.

An estimated **38** ..... racer snakes were found to be living on the island.

In 1996, a long-term conservation project was founded.

Questions 39 and 40

What still poses a threat to the snakes?

Choose ***TWO*** *letters* ***A–E.***

A disease
B the extent of its habitat
C severe weather events
D predation by rats
E expansion of tourism

39 .....

40 .....

READING TEST

SECTION 1

Questions 1–16

You should spend about 20 minutes on Questions 1–10, which are based on the text below.

How to get a grant for scientific research

In applying for a research grant, it's essential to start by identifying the appropriate granting body to contact for your proposal, as each body usually has its own particular priority areas. Once you've done this, check you can meet both the eligibility criteria and the deadline for the submission of applications. Your proposal should be written out in the format stipulated by your chosen organisation. Almost all granting bodies now have electronic application forms posted on the Internet, although these can sometimes be both complex and cumbersome.

A grant request is generally broken down into the following components:

Objectives

Succinctly describe your research goal, and what you propose to do to achieve this. It's a good idea to propose only those objectives that you feel relatively confident of achieving within the grant period. A proposal with too many objectives to be included in a relatively short time is likely to be considered over-ambitious, and might well be rejected, even if it involves cutting-edge science or a revolutionary new idea.

Background and rationale

Introduce the problem that the research intends to address. The length of your description is dictated by the length limitations on the application form. You should cover what is already known about the problem in the scientific literature, and highlight the major gaps or limitations in the current knowledge base. The final paragraph should state precisely what you will have achieved if the project succeeds, and the likely impact of a successful research project. In addition, many application forms, even for basic research grants, now have a section in which you're required to describe how the research is likely to contribute to economic development.

Experimental design and methods

You must describe in detail exactly what you're going to do to achieve your stated objectives. You should provide sufficient details to enable the review panel to critically evaluate your project. In particular, you must show how the experimental design will answer the questions that you're setting out to address; poor experimental design is the downfall of many applications.

Critical appraisal and limitations of the proposed approach

Describe the possible limitations of your proposed approach. For example, one of your proposed methodologies may have certain disadvantages that could impact adversely on your findings. A reviewer will certainly point this out and might find it sufficient grounds for rejecting your proposal. To meet such concerns, you should therefore state clearly that you're aware of the limitations of your approach, and if possible propose an alternative strategy if your first approach fails to deliver. You should also describe briefly any particular strengths of your laboratory likely to contribute to the success of the project if it is funded.

Questions 1–10

Do the following statements agree with the information given in the text?

In boxes 1–10 on your answer sheet, write

TRUE	*if the statement agrees with the information*
FALSE	*if the statement contradicts the information*
NOT GIVEN	*if there is no information on this*

1 Find the granting body which is best suited to the type of research you want to do.

2 Find out the date by which proposals must be sent in.

3 It's a good idea to lay out your proposal in an imaginative way.

4 Your proposal should have a long-term aim that extends beyond the timescale of the grant.

5 Make sure you fill all available space on the application form.

6 Your application should refer to other work already carried out on your topic.

7 It's essential to say how your research is relevant to economic and social issues.

8 The review panel may contact you with questions about your experimental design.

9 It's better to be honest if you have any doubts about aspects of your proposal.

10 You should give a full description of any laboratory facilities available to you.

Questions 11–16

The text on page 107 has six sections, **A–F.**

*Choose the correct heading for sections **A–F** from the list of headings below.*

Write the correct number (i–ix) in boxes 11–16 on your answer sheet.

List of Headings

i	Research experience
ii	Laboratory investigations
iii	Preliminary data
iv	Background reading
v	Description of the study area
vi	Data analysis
vii	Subject recruitment
viii	Collaboration
ix	Data collection

11 Section **A** .....

12 Section **B** .....

13 Section **C** .....

14 Section **D** .....

15 Section **E** .....

16 Section **F** .....

Experimental design and methods

Within this section of your research proposal, there should be several sub-sections, some of which are required for all types of grants, others of which are dependent on the topic of the research.

A Granting bodies like to see a concise description of the results of any work you have already carried out towards the research. Focus on the results that suggest that the proposed work will probably succeed.

B If the proposed research involves field studies, your application should include latitude and longitude, elevation, vegetation, rivers, rainy and dry seasons, mean rainfall and temperatures, and distance from the capital city.

C Describe how you plan to find people to take part in experiments and what criteria you will use for including or excluding particular individuals. Most importantly, include how you will obtain informed consent from these people, and which national authority or authorities have given ethical approval for your research.

D It is important to provide sufficient detail in this section for the reviewer to agree that the proposed work is feasible. There is no need to go into a lot of detail if the laboratory procedures that you plan to use are standard and widely described in scientific literature. However, you must still provide some details of your proposed procedures. Make sure you include a brief description of the various analytical techniques that you will carry out.

E This should include how it will be entered into a computerised database and what software will be used. In the case of trials, you should include how various variables, either continuous or discrete, will be compared among different groups studied using a variety of statistical methods, and how you intend to control for confounding variables.

F It is important to identify the partners with whom you intend to work, either in your own country or overseas. The choice of research partner or partners is crucial for your research project. They should provide complementary, rather than identical, expertise and/or facilities, and it must be clear how their presence will strengthen your proposal.

SECTION 2

Questions 17–27

You should spend about 20 minutes on Questions 17–27, which are based on the text below.

The world's oldest mattress

A study published in *Science* by Lyn Wadley of the University of Witwatersrand and her colleagues throws new light on the behaviour of early man in South Africa. The focus of the research is a cave in a natural rock shelter called Sibudu, situated in a sandstone cliff, 40 kilometres north of Durban. Dr Wadley has found evidence for at least 15 separate occasions when it acted as a home, with periods in between when it was abandoned, as is often the case with such shelters. Each occupation left debris behind, though, and as this accumulated, the cave floor gradually rose. All told, these layers reveal occupation over a period of about 40,000 years.

Among the things Dr Wadley's team found in the floor of the cave was evidence of mat making throughout the period of habitation. The oldest stratum, dating from 77,000 years ago, predate other known instances of plant matting by approximately 50,000 years. They consisted of compacted stems and leaves of plants stacked in layers within a chunk of sediment three metres thick.

'The inhabitants would have collected the plant matter from along the river, located directly below the site, and laid the plants on the floor of the shelter,' said Wadley. The lower part of these layers, compressed to a thickness of about a centimetre, consists of sedges, rushes and grasses. The upper part, just under a millimetre thick, is made of leaves from *Cryptocarya woodii*, a tree whose foliage contains chemicals that kill biting insects. Dr Wadley thus thinks that what she has found are mattresses on which the inhabitants slept, although they may also have walked and worked on them.

The upshot is another piece of evidence of how, around this period, humans were creating a range of hitherto unknown artefacts. Adhesives, arrows, needles, ochre-decorated pictograms and necklaces made from shells are all contemporary with Dr Wadley's finds, and stone tools became more delicate and sophisticated during this period.

Indeed, given the age of the mats and other artefacts at the site, it's clear that *Homo sapiens* was the hominid who slept in the cave. The earliest hominids had very different sleeping accommodations. Even though they had evolved an efficient way to walk on the ground, hominids such as *Australopithecus* were still small, not much bigger than a chimpanzee. They probably settled in trees at night, for if they slept on the ground, they would have been vulnerable to nocturnal predators looking for a midnight meal. The fossils of early hominids indicate this was possible; they still retained features useful for climbing, such as curved fingers and long arms. Once in the trees, they probably built nests of branches, twigs and leaves, just as chimpanzees do today.

The first hominid to try the ground as a bed might have been *Homo erectus*, starting almost two million years ago. Richard Wrangham, a biological anthropologist at Harvard University, suggests that once hominids learned how to control fire they discovered they could sleep on the ground while the flames kept predators away. It was also useful for cooking and processing foods, allowing *Homo erectus* to expand its diet. Adaptations for arboreal life were eventually lost, and *Homo erectus* became bigger and taller, the first hominid with a more modern body plan. Although there's no evidence in the paleontological record that hints at what type of bedding *Homo erectus* used, modern humans were certainly not the only hominids to construct 'mattresses'. Neanderthals were also building grass beds, based on evidence from a cave site in Spain dating to between 53,000 and 39,000 years ago.

Questions 17–19

Choose the correct letter, ***A, B, C*** *or* ***D.***

Write your answers in boxes 17–19 on your answer sheet.

17 Dr Wadley believes that the cave at Sibudu was lived in
- **A** continuously over many thousands of years.
- **B** on a surprising number of different occasions.
- **C** intermittently during a long period of pre-history.
- **D** at times when other dwellings had to be abandoned.

18 Why is the evidence of mat making at Sibudu particularly significant?
- **A** It reflects findings in similar caves elsewhere.
- **B** It's older than other examples of similar craft skills.
- **C** It proves that the caves were actually once inhabited.
- **D** It helps establish the period when the caves were in use.

19 What leads Dr Wadley to think that the mats were used for sleeping?
- **A** one of the materials from which they were made
- **B** the thickness of the strata that were created
- **C** the use of plant matter collected nearby
- **D** the fact they were constructed in layers

Questions 20–22

What other artefacts from the same period as Sibudu are mentioned in the text?

Write the correct three letters ***A–G*** *in boxes 20–22 on your answer sheet.*

- **A** illustrations
- **B** building materials
- **C** weapons
- **D** sewing equipment
- **E** fastenings for clothing
- **F** cooking equipment
- **G** cleaning materials

20 .....

21 .....

22 .....

Questions 23–27

Complete the sentences below.

Choose ***NO MORE THAN TWO WORDS*** *from the passage for each answer.*

Write your answers in boxes 23–27 on your answer sheet.

Australopithecus probably used **23** ..... as places to sleep.

Early hominids had physical features that suggest they were good at **24** ..... .

Early hominids may have constructed nests similar to those made by **25** ..... .

Homo erectus used **26** ..... for protection whilst sleeping.

Neanderthals may have used **27** ..... to make a surface to sleep on.

SECTION 3

Questions 28–40

You should spend about 20 minutes on Questions 28–40, which are based on the text below.

BRIGHT LIGHTS, BUG CITY

In the heart of Africa's savannah, there is a city built entirely from natural, biodegradable materials, and it's a model of sustainable development. Its curved walls, graceful arches and towers are rather beautiful too. It's no human city, of course. It's a termite mound.

Unlike termites and other nest-building insects, humans pay little attention to making buildings fit for their environments. As we wake up to climate change and resource depletion, though, interest in how insects manage their built environments is growing, and we have a lot to learn. 'The building mechanisms and the design principles that make the properties of insect nests possible aren't well understood,' says Guy Theraulaz of the Research Centre on Animal Cognition in France. That's not for want of trying. Research into termite mounds kicked off in the 1960s, when Swiss entomologist Martin Liischer made groundbreaking studies of nests created by termites of the genus *Macrotermes* on the plains of southern Africa.

It was Liischer who suggested the chaotic-looking mounds were in fact exquisitely engineered eco-constructions. Specifically, he proposed an intimate connection between how the mounds are built and what the termites eat. *Macrotermes* species live on cellulose, a constituent of plant matter that humans can't digest. In fact, neither can termites. They get round this by cultivating gardens for fungi, which can turn it into digestible nutrients. These areas must be well ventilated, their temperature and humidity closely controlled – no mean feat in the tropical climates in which termites live. In Liischer's theory, heat from the fungi's metabolism and the termites' bodies causes stagnant air, laden with carbon dioxide, to rise up a central chimney. From there it fans out through the porous walls of the mound, while new air is sucked in at the base.

This simple and appealing idea spawned at least one artificial imitation: the Eastgate Centre in Harare, Zimbabwe, designed by architect Mick Pearce, which boasts a termite-inspired ventilation and cooling system. It turns out, however, that few if any termite mounds work this way.

Scott Turner, a termite expert at The State University of New York, and Rupert Soar of Freeform Engineering in Nottingham, UK, looked into the design principles of *Macrotermes* mounds in Namibia. They found that the mounds' walls are warmer than the central nest, which rules out the kind of buoyant outward flow of CO_2-rich air proposed by Liischer. Indeed, injecting a tracer gas into the mound showed little evidence of steady, convective air circulation.

Turner and Soar believe that termite mounds instead tap turbulence in the gusts of wind that hit them. A single breath of wind contains small eddies and currents that vary in speed and direction with different frequencies. The outer walls of the mounds are built to allow only eddies changing with low frequencies to penetrate deep within them. As the range of frequencies in the wind changes from gust to gust, the boundary between the stale air in the nest and the fresh air from outside moves about within the mounds' walls, allowing the two bodies of air to be exchanged. In essence, the mound functions as a giant lung.

This is very different to the way ventilation works in modern human buildings, where fresh air is blown in through vents to flush stale air out. Turner thinks there's something to be gleaned from the termites' approach. 'We could turn the whole idea of the wall on its head,' he says. 'We shouldn't think of walls as barriers to stop the outside getting in, but rather design them as adaptive, porous interfaces that regulate the exchange of heat and air between the inside and outside. Instead of opening a window to let fresh air in, it would be the wall that does it, but carefully filtered and managed the way termite mounds do it.'

Turner's ideas were among many discussed at a workshop on insect architecture organised by Theraulaz in Venice, Italy, last year. It aimed to pool understanding from a range of disciplines, from experts in insect behaviour to practising architects. 'Some real points of contact began to emerge,' says Turner. 'There was a prevailing idea among the biologists that architects could learn much from us. I think the opposite is also true.' One theme was just how proficient termites are at adapting their buildings to local conditions. Termites in very hot climates, for example, embed their mounds deep in the soil – a hugely effective way of regulating temperature. 'As we come to understand more, it opens up a vast universe of new bio-inspired design principles,' says Turner. Such approaches are the opposite of modern human ideas of design and control, in which a central blueprint is laid down in advance by an architect and rigidly stuck to. But Turner thinks we could find ourselves adopting a more insect-like approach as technological advances make it feasible.

Questions 28–34

Complete the notes below.

Choose ***NO MORE THAN THREE WORDS AND/OR A NUMBER*** *from the text for each answer.*

Write your answers in boxes 28–34 on your answer sheet.

Liischer's model of *Macrotermes* mounds

Termites rely on **28** ..... as their source of food.

Termites create areas of fungi called **29** ..... .

The fungi produce **30** ..... for the termites.

Both fungi and termites produce **31** ..... and stale air.

Stale air goes up a structure called the **32** ..... .

Carbon dioxide escapes through the walls of the mound.

Fresh air then enters at the **33** ..... of the mound.

The whole process provides ventilation for the fungi, and manages both the **34** ..... and temperature of their area.

Questions 35–40

Do the following statements agree with the information given in the text?

In boxes 35–40 on your answer sheet, write

TRUE	*if the statement agrees with the information*
FALSE	*if the statement contradicts the information*
NOT GIVEN	*if there is no information on this*

35 Pearce's design in Zimbabwe was an attempt to put Liischer's ideas into practice.

36 Turner and Soar's research disproved Liischer's theory.

37 Turner and Soar built a model termite mound to test their ideas.

38 Turner likens the mechanism for changing the air in the mound to an organ in the human body.

39 Turner thinks it unlikely that the termites' way of ventilating their mounds would work in a human building.

40 Turner believes that biologists have little to learn from architects.

WRITING TEST

TASK 1

You should spend about 20 minutes on this task.

You have recently gone to live in a new city.

Write a letter to your English-speaking friend. In your letter
- *explain why you have gone to live in the new city*
- *describe the place where you are living*
- *invite your friend to come and see you*

Write at least 150 words.

You do not need to write any addresses.

Begin your letter like this:

Dear Anna,

TASK 2

You should spend about 40 minutes on this task.

Write about this topic.

The ownership of cars should be restricted to one per family in order to reduce traffic congestion and pollution.

To what extent do you agree or disagree?

Give reasons for your answer and include any relevant examples from your own knowledge or experience.

Write at least 250 words.

SPEAKING TEST

PART 1 – INTRODUCTION AND INTERVIEW

Let's talk about how you keep in touch with world events.
- How do you usually find out what is happening in the world?
- Are you more interested in national news or world news? Why (not)?
- What do you do if you want to find out more details about a news item (and why)?
- Do you think reading or listening to the news in English is a good idea?

PART 2 – INDIVIDUAL LONG TURN

Candidate Task Card

> Describe a time when you took part in an experiment or a piece of research.
>
> You should say:
> what the aim of the experiment or piece of research was
> why you became involved in it
> what your role in it was
> and explain how you felt about taking part.

You will have to talk about the topic for one to two minutes.

You will have one minute to think about what you are going to say.

You can make some notes to help you if you wish.

Rounding off questions
- Do you know what the outcome of the experiment/research was?
- Would you take part in that sort of experiment/research again?

PART 3 – TWO-WAY DISCUSSION

Let's consider first of all the role of scientific research.
- How important is scientific research?
- Which type of scientific research do you think is most important (and why)?
- Do you think too much money is spent on exploring outer space? Why (not)?

Finally, let's talk about how scientific research is reported by the media.
- Do you think that the media reports scientific research accurately? Why (not)?

Audioscripts

Unit 1

1.1

P = Presenter, E = Expert

P: I'd like to ask you two questions: what is the real reason for the ageing population? And secondly, and more importantly, what effect is this having on relationships in society?

E: Well, there's not just one reason; there are a number of them. Firstly, the birth rate has declined over the last 20 years – fewer babies are being born. The second reason is that 60 years ago, there was a baby boom; these 'baby boomers' are now reaching retirement age. There's also no doubt about people's improved diet: more is known about healthy and unhealthy eating, and food producers are obliged to give consumers more information about the fat and salt content of their food. In fact, I'd say in general people have a healthier lifestyle: not only do they eat better, they have also been educated in the right way to exercise and keep fit. Lastly, we can't underestimate the enormous progress that has been made in the field of medicine. These advances have increased life expectancy to around 80 in the developed world. People are also given routine vaccinations against life-threatening diseases … for example, flu jabs for the elderly.

P: And what are the social consequences of this ageing population – that in the West the younger generation is now being outnumbered by the old?

E: The main result is that, in the future, a smaller number of young people will have to support this older population. For all of us, that means working longer, spending more time caring for old people, and paying more social insurance to fund their medical treatment. But of course, it also puts a strain on family relationships. Parents find that, having spent 20 years bringing up their own children, they then spend the next ten looking after their ageing parents – often both sets. That means less time together as a couple and less free time to enjoy with other friends and family. It's not easy …

1.4

1 I think my parents' generation has been quite lucky.

2 My parents worked hard all their lives, but they both retired when they were 60 and they've been given good pensions. So now they can relax and enjoy themselves.

3 They've said that they don't want to be a burden on us, and that we children aren't expected to look after them when they get old.

4 Considering that my husband and I are now being asked to work until we are 68, I'm glad they said that.

1.5

P = Presenter, L = Lauren

P: I know that Vietnam is a country which is developing incredibly fast and Lauren, you've just been sent on a three-week trip there as part of your university course …

L: That's right, yes.

P: ... which sounds fantastic. I wish my economics degree had included that kind of trip, but ... Can you just tell us a bit about how people in Vietnam are adapting to those huge changes and what it all means for them?

L: Sure. As you say, Vietnam is a very dynamic society right now. It's being transformed at an amazingly fast rate – both economically and socially. We were really lucky to get to experience that first-hand and get to meet so many different people of all ages, from all kinds of work backgrounds – politicians and government officials, farmers, and so many just ... regular people too. And I've got to say – if anyone's thinking of going there – the people are amazing: really warm and friendly. But to answer your question, I think what you have is an older generation who are very conscious of their history. Many of them have been through two wars and are very aware of how much they've struggled to get to this point now of … of relative prosperity. And then there's a younger generation and they don't necessarily see all that effort. They kind of take this new wealth and opportunity for granted. I think they see the world opening up and they really want a part of it … And that's not always easy, because there are still some restrictions on access to information – Facebook and other social networking sites are closed down from time to time, for example. On the other side, the older generation desperately want their children and grandchildren to understand Vietnam's history and be proud of it … and of course to respect Vietnamese traditions.

P: And did you get a sense that people are confused by this? That they don't know which way to turn, as it were?

L: You know, not really. The sense I got was that the gap between old and young is being bridged by the generation in the middle – I guess the 30 and 40-somethings. We spent a day in a fishing community near the Mekong Delta and we had a meal with a family there, and all the generations were getting on fine together ... I had the impression that the parents kind of balanced the home. The grandparents are really included and involved in things – they get to take care of the grandchildren and to teach them what they know. You could see that really clearly. And at the same time, the grandparents are definitely listened to and treated with respect by the parents and the children. I was really impressed by that, especially when you compare it with ...

1.8

B = Ben, S = Sam

B: Hi Sam. Fancy bumping into you here. I've been wondering how you were.

S: Oh, hi Ben. What a nice surprise. I'm fine. I've been working in Scotland for the last three months.

B: Well, it obviously suits you. You're looking very well. Have you decided to move up there?

S: No, it's just a temporary job. I've been helping to renovate an old castle. And how's it all going with you? Is Emily well?

B: Yes, thanks. She's just finished her nursing course.

S: Really? That's fantastic. Do give her my best regards.

B: Well, great to see you. I should probably go and do my shopping.

S: OK. Could I have your phone number again? I've lost it.

B: Sure. It's 07945 699636.

S: Thanks. Well, speak soon I hope. Good luck with the job.

1.10

F = Friend, MA = Model answer

1

F: Hi. What a nice surprise! How are you?

MA: I'm fine, thanks. Good to see you.

2

F: So, what have you been up to lately?

MA: I've been working quite hard, but everything's going well.

3
F: Well, it obviously suits you. You're looking well.
MA: Thanks. So are you.
4
F: And do you see much of the old crowd these days?
MA: I've seen Polly a few times.
5
F: Well, I don't mean to be rude, but I need to get to the bank.
MA: No problem. Great to see you.

Unit 2

1.12

1 The setting for Alain de Botton's thought-provoking book, *A Week at the Airport*, is Heathrow airport.
2 The characters are you and me and every other typical passenger that passes through the airport.
3 The book is based on conversations that the author had with travellers and airline staff.
4 The idea behind it is that if you are looking for somewhere that can portray modern civilisation, you don't need to look any further than an airport.

1.13

On April 25, 2003, Aron Ralston drove to Moab, Utah, where he mountain-biked the famous Slickrock Trail. He then made his way to Horseshoe Canyon. When he arrived, night was falling, so he made camp. He was planning an ascent of Mount McKinley in Alaska, and this trip was part of his training. In the morning, he filled his backpack with water, candy bars and his climbing gear, and set out for Bluejohn Canyon.

He climbed into the canyon on April 26. He had gone about five miles when he came to a section where a series of large boulders were hanging, wedged between the walls of the canyon. He worked his way past these until he came to a boulder hanging over a drop of about three metres. Putting one hand around the boulder, which weighed about 800 pounds, Ralston stretched to reach a secure foothold below. As he did so, the boulder rotated, slid down and trapped his right hand between it and the canyon wall, crushing it completely.

His heart was beating fast and for the first few moments he threw his body repeatedly against the boulder to move it, but it refused to move. He forced himself to stop, breathe and then considered his situation logically.

He hadn't told anyone where he was. It would be days before anyone realised that he was missing. Ralston was standing on a small stone, facing the boulder that had crushed his hand. The pain was intense, but he was determined to stay in control. He only had two courses of action left to him: he could chip at the rock to free his hand; or he could cut off his hand.

His only tool was a cheap multi-tool. Over the next days, he worked to chip away at the rock with it, but the progress he made was minimal. He was wearing shorts, hiking boots and a fleece pullover. He had started with three litres of water. Now he was down to one.

Ralston had been waiting there for five days. But by the time the search teams started out, he had long since decided what he had to do. He packed his gear and arranged everything neatly in preparation for cutting off his hand. The arm was numb, so he didn't feel anything, but it was still not an easy thing to do. The operation took over an hour. Dripping blood, he made his way back out of the canyon and began the long hike out of the National Park. After six miles, he was met by some tourists.

1.14

1 I hadn't been there before.
2 You are allowed to smoke.
3 It isn't the first time this has happened.
4 She was the person I told you about.
5 They weren't as tired from the journey as I expected.
6 I was talking about what happened to me.
7 She had been waiting a long time.
8 I haven't spoken French for years.

1.15

Part 1

Oscar Wilde's collection of short stories *The Happy Prince and other Stories* is ostensibly for children, but like all good children's literature, the stories have been written in a way that transcends age: their meaning is just as relevant for adults as it is for children. The stories contain elements of a traditional fairy tale – giants, speaking animals, perhaps a message too – but they are more than just good stories. They have a lyrical quality and a beauty … often this beauty lies in their sadness. I remember being quite upset by them as a child and when I re-read them to my children some 30 years later, I still had to keep back the tears. In fact, it's impossible not to be moved by them. When I said they had a message, I should qualify that by saying that Oscar Wilde kept from giving moral lessons. He simply threw light on human behaviour and then left the reader to make up their own mind. Let me give you an example – the story of *The Happy Prince*.

Part 2

The Happy Prince is a statue that stands high in the square of an old town in northern Europe. It's a fine statue covered in gold leaf and decorated with jewels for eyes and jewels in his sword. From where he stands, he can keep abreast of all that's happening in the town, good and bad. One day, a little swallow arrives, flying on its way south to a warmer climate in Egypt for the winter. He stops to rest on the shoulder of the Happy Prince and the prince asks him for his help. He persuades the swallow to take the gold and jewels from his statue to various people in need around the town: a little boy selling matches in the street, a poor artist in his cold attic room. The swallow stays for some days keeping the prince company and doing good errands for him until he has taken all the gold and jewels from the statue. Unfortunately for the swallow, it has got too late and too cold for it to continue its journey and it dies at the foot of the statue. The town councillors come by and see the statue all grey and plain-looking with a dead bird lying at its feet, and thinking it's an eyesore, they decide to pull it down and melt it so that the metal can be turned into something useful. The workers at the metal foundry find one part won't melt – the Happy Prince's heart – and they throw it on the rubbish tip where the dead swallow is lying.

1.16

See track 1.15, Part 1

1.17

See track 1.15, Part 2

1.18

A = Friend 1, B = Friend 2

A: How was the trip?

B: Well, we had a great time once we got there, but the journey there was a complete nightmare.

A: Oh, no. Poor you! What happened?

B: Well, about four hours before we were due to leave, Hannah realised that her passport was out of date.

A: Oh, that's awful. So did you leave her behind?

B: No, Paul took her straight to the passport office in London and someone had just cancelled their appointment, so they were able to get Hannah a new passport within an hour.

A: That was a stroke of luck. And where were you?

B: I went to the airport to wait for them and kept in touch with them by phone.

A: How stressful! Did they make it in time?

B: Well, they wouldn't have done but the plane was delayed by two hours, so in the end they got there with a bit of time to spare. But my nerves were completely destroyed by then.

A: I can sympathise. I hate being late when I'm travelling. Did the rest of the trip go OK?

B: Yeah, it was great, thanks. Costa Rica was fabulous. But I made sure we got to the airport four hours early for the flight back.

A: Did you? I don't blame you. I think I would have done the same thing …

1.21

F = Friend, MA = Model answer

1

F: You'll never guess what happened to me yesterday on the bus. I started talking to this woman who I thought was Sue, my next-door neighbour, about my problems at work. But it wasn't Sue, it was a complete stranger!

MA: How embarrassing! When did you realise it wasn't Sue?

2

F: I thought I'd lost my wallet this morning. But I'd actually left it on the table at a café and some kind person handed it in.

MA: That was lucky.

3

F: I feel really bad. Jeff asked me if he could borrow my camera and I said 'no'. The thing is he's really clumsy and it's a £600 camera.

MA: Don't worry about it. I think I would have done the same thing.

4

F: We had some people round to dinner last night and we spent so long chatting that I forgot to turn the oven off and all the food I had prepared was completely ruined. It was all dry and burnt.

MA: What a nightmare! What did you do?

5

F: My credit card got stuck in the cash machine. I phoned the bank and cancelled the card, and also left a note with my phone number in case someone managed to get it out.

MA: That was good thinking.

Unit 3

1.22

There's a group of philanthropists in the US – Gates, Buffett, Rockefeller, etcetera – who have contributed a lot of money to good causes over the last fifteen years. The problem for them is that because they're so rich and powerful, people get suspicious of their motives. So, when they meet up, they often do so secretly, like they did a few years ago in Manhattan.

1.23

P = Presenter, D = Didier Bertrand

P: I'm here with Didier Bertrand from the Research Department of GNH electricity company and today we're talking about 'smart homes' of the future. Everyone has heard about this type of technology in one form or another – robots that clean the house; cookers which will be making our meals for us – and, in a few years, I'm sure we will have heard a lot more. But what we'd all like to know is firstly, what technology is actually just around the corner – not just some techie's or researcher's pipe dream – and secondly, what things are actually practical and useful, and what are just gimmicks. So, first of all, welcome, Didier ...

D: Hello.

P: Let's talk about what gadgets our homes will have and I'd like you to tell me if these are a reality, a possibility or just science fiction.

D: OK.

P: 'Intelligent' fridges.

D: Yes, intelligent kitchen gadgets and appliances are here already, but intelligent fridges are only in a few richer homes. I think we'll all be using them when food producers make the packaging intelligent too – so that the fridge can tell you when your food is going bad.

P: So, a reality then, that one. What about ultrasonic showers?

D: Well, the need is already here. In the next ten years or so, water shortages will have become a big problem, so we need to find alternatives. And we already know that sound waves are very effective at cleaning, but whether they're safe or not for humans remains to be proven. Ultrasound is certainly something we will be looking at, but ...

P: A possibility then?

D: A remote one, I think, but a possibility, yes. There's another thing we are working on with sound.

P: What's that?

D: It's sound-proofing using energy fields. At the moment, if you want to sound-proof a room you use insulation, but in the future people will be using energy fields that isolate a particular space from the rest of the house. So you will be able to play music as loudly as you want in one room without disturbing anyone else.

P: That sounds amazing. What about surfaces in the house that are intelligent?

D: Yes, that's a very interesting area. We're working on several things – for example, kitchen surfaces that transmit heat – so that when you put a frozen pizza down in a certain smart, or intelligent, packaging, it'll defrost automatically. I don't think people will be cleaning kitchen surfaces either in the future – they'll be self-cleaning. And another area of development ... we'll soon be installing walls and surfaces in each room that can act as computer or TV screens so that you can move around the house to do your computing or to watch TV.

P: That technology is quite real then?

D: Yes, I think in ten years or so, that kind of technology will have become quite common in new-build houses.

P: Wow! Anything else we haven't mentioned?

D: I think people will be able to control light much more intelligently. Our company will be launching a new system for bedrooms next year that simulates the sunrise.

P: I see, so you wake up gradually as the sun comes up ... gets brighter.

D: Exactly …

1.24

1 The weekday edition of *The New York Times* contains more information than the average person in 17th-century England learned in a lifetime.

2 Around a thousand books are published internationally every day and the total of all printed knowledge doubles every five years.
3 More information has been published in the last 30 years than in the previous 5,000.

1.25
In 2007, the number of people dying from drinking unclean water was a shocking 6,000 per day. Diarrhoea is one of the biggest killers of children in the developing world, a situation that can be changed through the use of vaccines and the drinking of clean water. An ingenious invention, the *Lifestraw*, may be one answer.

Developed by the non-profit making organisation Vestergaard Frandsen, based in Switzerland, this simple device has won a number of awards including *Time Magazine's* Best Innovation of the Year.

Like all good inventions, *Lifestraw* works on a very simple principle. Water is sucked by the user through a filter that traps 99.9% of all water-borne bacteria, including salmonella and E. coli. As a result, it provides protection against the killer diseases cholera and typhoid, as well as common stomach infections like dysentery and diarrhoea.

The filter contains a substance called PuroTech Disinfecting Resin, or PDR, a material which kills bacteria on contact. Pre-filters made of textile fabric first remove particles up to 15 microns. Each filter lasts up to a year, and has a cleaning capacity of 700 litres of water. This equates to a typical daily intake of two litres of water per day. *Lifestraw* is only 30 cm long and being made of plastic, it weighs very little, so it can be worn around the neck without any discomfort to the wearer. Each device costs around US $6.

What are the limitations of *Lifestraw*? Not many it seems. It shouldn't be shared by users, of course. It isn't effective at filtering out metals such as iron and arsenic. And if you use it with salt water, you will reduce its life by about half. And people who are sensitive or allergic to iodine should seek advice before they use it. Other than that, there are only positives, the main one being that it doesn't run on electrical power but works simply through the mechanical action of sucking. There are some tips for making it work better, for example by sucking very steadily on the straw, or by periodically blowing some air and water back through it to clean out the filters, but basically it's obvious how it works.

Lifestraw was used successfully in the Haiti earthquake disaster of 2010 and the Pakistan floods of the same year. Like all ideas – particularly those aimed at solving humanitarian problems – it has its sceptics. The charity WaterAid said that while in principle it was a great idea, it did not solve the fundamental problem of access to water for many people in developing countries, which was one of distance, not cleanliness – many people have to walk up to 30 kilometres a day to get water.

1.28
A = Andy, M = Meg
A: Can you give me a hand? I'm having trouble sending this document.
M: What do you want to do exactly?
A: Nothing very complicated. I'm trying to attach this document to an email and it won't let me.
M: Let me have a look. OK, I see – the document's too large.
A: Hmm … I thought it might be. The trouble is it's got a lot of photos in it, and I can't just cut them.
M: No, well you can compress the photos.
A: What does that involve?
M: I'll show you. Right-click on the photo … then select format … then compress … then select 'print resolution'. If you do that with all of them, that should do the trick.
A: Yes, I see, but then that reduces the quality of the photos, doesn't it? What else do you suggest?
M: Umm … Have you tried dividing the document into three or four separate documents?
A: No, I'll give that a try and see if it works.
M: OK. Feel free to ask if you want me to help you compress the photos after all.
A: Yeah, OK. Thanks.

1.30
F = Friend, MA = Model answer
1
F: Can you help me? My presentation slides look really boring!
MA: OK. What do you want to do exactly?
2
F: Well, my slides are just full of text, and they look very plain and uninteresting. I want to make them more attractive.
MA: Let me have a look. Yes, I see. Well, you can add some animations.
3
F: What does that involve?
MA: Well, I'll show you. You have to select some of the text and then choose a way to animate it from the list of options.
4
F: That sounds a bit complicated. What else do you suggest?
MA: Have you tried just changing the font and the colour of the text?
5
F: No, that's a good idea. I'll give that a try.
MA: OK. Feel free to ask me if you need more help.

Unit 4

1.31
1 First of all, just a few words of thanks.
2 Most of the time, it's a bit of a laugh.
3 As a matter of fact, he's a friend of mine.
4 That's kind of you, but it seems like a lot of trouble.
5 Of course it was just a bit of fun.
6 In spite of that, there were a number of volunteers.

1.32
P = Presenter; H = Handy; G = Guy Francis
P: Welcome to the *Topical Hour*. In the second part of the programme, we'll be looking at the question of the long-term unemployed. Is each case different or are there measures we can take that will help all unemployed people get back to work? But first, following the news that the graffiti artist 'Tox' has been convicted of vandalism for his graffiti, we ask, 'When is graffiti art and when is it vandalism?' I'm joined by Guy Francis, former arts correspondent for the *Daily News*, and Handy, a graffiti artist himself. So both are experts in their own way on the subject. First of all, Handy, what was your reaction to this conviction?
H: I thought it was outrageous – he's gone to prison for his art. How can you say that one graffiti artist's work is vandalism and another's is art? Would you let the courts decide what artwork deserved to be shown in a gallery and what didn't? Of course not. There's no difference in this case.
P: Handy's right, isn't he? Graffiti is either art or vandalism. You can't have it both ways. Guy Francis.

G: Well, that's true, if the graffiti is in a place where the owner agrees to have it there. If Tox had put his work in a gallery, as Handy just suggested, there wouldn't have been any trouble. The fact is, he put his name all over public and private property. Every owner of that property complained and said that their property had been vandalised. In other words, Tox had caused criminal damage. People classed it as damage because all Tox does is to write his name and the year in numbers on the property over and over again. There are no imaginative images at all.
P: So, you're saying that if the owner of a property likes the work that a graffiti artist puts on his wall, then it's art.
G: Well, I'm saying in that case it's *not* vandalism. The whole debate of whether it's art or not is a different matter. If you take a famous and well-loved graffiti artist like Banksy, whose work sells for tens of thousands of pounds, you can't imagine the owner of a property complaining if some of Banksy's work appeared on his wall. Either type of graffiti could be considered art – but in the eyes of the law, whether or not it's vandalism is up to the owner.

1.33

1 The message was clear: is this how far we have come since the Stone Age?
2 Often it carries a political or social message, but in an amusing way that ordinary people can relate to.
3 Despite not calling himself an artist, his work has been shown in galleries and has sold for thousands of dollars.
4 Banksy, who is based in the UK, is perhaps the world's best-known graffiti artist.
5 Banksy loves to surprise. In 2005, a picture showing a primitive human being pushing a shopping cart appeared in the British Museum.

1.34

Speaker 1
You see, there are some places that have a strong tradition of a particular kind of music that, if you were born there, you just can't disassociate yourself from, wherever else in the world you may go. I was born in Mississippi and brought up on country music. Country music tells stories about real life: about love, pain, family, fortune and misfortune. Those are things that everyday folk can relate to and I think it's one of the last genres of music that's in touch with human feelings in that way. It's not just about money and having a good time (though of course that comes into it sometimes), or about politics. It's not insulting or angry in the way that rap music can be. It's about home.

Speaker 2
I think music often plays a more significant role in the culture of poorer communities. When you live in an area which is poor and deprived, you have to get your fun cheap. Music and dance can do that. That's why in Brazil dance music is such an important part of our culture. It's also to do with our history. There are so many different ethnic groups in Brazil that we have a big range of musical influences to draw on: local Indian instruments which are still used today, African rhythms, the melancholy songs of the Portuguese settlers. They've come together to create unique styles of music like samba, carimbó, bossa nova, maracatu. That mixture also brings people together. That's the power music has. You can see that so clearly at Carnaval.

Speaker 3
You don't have to be able to sing or play music to express your feelings through it. Millions of teenagers have been able to express their feelings of frustration at not being understood, or of boredom or anger, or of wanting to break free from the pressures of school and home, by listening to rock music. They hear the very same sentiments they're feeling expressed in lyrics that are supported by a compelling tune or beat. I was brought up with punk rock, which was a kind of do-it-yourself, non-commercial, fast rock music. The music was saying, 'We reject all this commercial packaged stuff you're trying to sell us. Let's just keep the music simple and honest.' And it hit a chord with us, for sure.

Speaker 4
I love hip-hop. I love that it came from just ordinary, average people who wanted to make a better life for themselves from music. I love the innovative side of it too: that people figured out how to make new sounds using old technology – and some new technology too – but they took limited resources and came up with something totally new. No one ever demanded that hip-hop was played on radio or at clubs; there were no restrictions on what it could do or say. Forget the commercial version of hip-hop you hear today – 'cos it doesn't count for anything – the original hip-hop meant living free in an urban environment.

1.35

I = Ian, S = Sue
I: Hey, Sue, did you see that brilliant documentary on TV last night?
S: No. What was it about?
I: It was about the Amazon …
S: Oh, a nature documentary … not really my kind of thing, actually. I know I should take more of an interest, but I never feel particularly inspired by them. So what was so good about it?
I: Well I'm a big fan of the presenter, Bruce Parry – you must have seen him, he's been on TV a lot recently. Well, he travels the length of the Amazon interviewing different people who live and work around the river – so not just the indigenous tribes that have lived there for centuries, but also more recent settlers, like loggers and farmers.
S: Yes, I know Bruce Parry. He did that *Tribe* series where he went to live with different tribes in Africa and places. It got on my nerves a bit actually …
I: How can you say that? I have a lot of time for Bruce Parry. I could listen to him all day! Anyway, what I liked about this documentary was that he listened to everyone's side of the story – even the loggers who are tearing down the Amazon Forest. He doesn't make any judgements – the viewer is just left to make up their own mind ...
S: Well, it sounds quite good … I guess I just get a bit tired of people making these programmes supposedly about other people living in difficult conditions, but more often it's just about them …

1.37

F = Friend, MA = Model answer
1
F: What do you think of mobile phones with loud music ringtones?
MA: They really get on my nerves, especially when one starts ringing on the train or bus.
2
F: Do you like graffiti?
MA: I'm not particularly keen on graffiti, but I've seen a few pieces that I like.
3
F: Do you like going to musicals?
MA: Yes, I love going to the theatre, but I don't get many opportunities.
4
F: What's your favourite TV programme?
MA: I'm really into watching sports. I'm a big fan of Formula One racing.

5
F: What kind of music do you listen to? Rock or something else?
MA: No, rock music isn't really my kind of thing. I'm into country and western music.

Unit 5

1.38
If you visit the famous French Quarter in New Orleans – which, after the airport, is probably the only part that most tourists see – everything now seems to be back to normal. That's because the French Quarter was largely spared when Hurricane Katrina hit in 2005. There was some damage, but it was fairly quickly repaired. But if you go to one of the residential areas south-east of the centre, it's a different story: you keep on seeing the effects of the disaster, even this long after the storm. There are a lot of homes and neighbourhoods which still have to be rebuilt. It wasn't the winds that did the damage, but rather the flood waters when the city's levees failed to hold the big tidal wave back. Huge numbers of people were forced to leave. A few people decided to resettle elsewhere, but most New Orleanians would never consider leaving their beloved city. About two-thirds of the residents have managed to return and little by little they are rebuilding the city.

The redevelopment plan has not been systematic or co-ordinated. There are some federal projects, some state projects, volunteer groups and also projects run by private benefactors. A particularly interesting project is taking place down in the Lower 9th Ward, an area that was pretty depressed even before the storm. A well-known film actor, used his own money to create a non-profit organisation called 'Make it right'. Using architects from all over America, they planned to build 150 safe and environmentally-friendly homes in the area where ordinary local people could afford to buy or rent.

All the houses contain innovative design and safety features, because no one wants to see their home flood again. One solution is the 'float house' – the base of the house can rise on two guide posts and act as a raft in case of floods.

I visited some of them myself and was impressed by the imaginativeness of the architecture. At the same time, you can't help wondering how many more homes could have been built if they had used simpler designs and materials. It's a difficult issue. Here's someone genuinely trying to help people rebuild their lives, but is their vision too ambitious? Some critics think it's impractical.

1.39
The fact that most people have returned says a lot about how special this city is. The people who live here can't imagine living anywhere else.

I'm a musician and making a living in New Orleans has always been a challenge. We hoped to see more investment in jobs and tourism after the hurricane.

But since Hurricane Katrina, life has definitely become harder. I love this city, but these days, I'm forced to go out of town to find work.

1.40
China – minor
found – drowned
front – hunt
meant – sent
ocean – motion
placed – taste
rule – tool
way – weigh
whale – they'll
where – share

1.41
P = Presenter, J = Jim Bradstock
P: According to the McKinsey Global Institute, '350 million people will be added to China's urban population by 2025. China will have 221 cities with one million-plus living in them – Europe currently has 35.' That's a lot of people, a lot of energy and a lot of pollution. So the race is on to design and build sustainable cities that can generate their own energy, collect their own water and recycle their own waste. Pollution in these new eco-cities is not an option. I asked architect Jim Bradstock whether such cities are a realistic possibility or still some urban planners' pipe dream. Jim ...
J: There's a saying in China: 'Anything is possible, but nothing is easy.' The thing is that there are a lot of good designs and clever ideas – take your pick. But you also need the political will to make it happen, and a huge co-ordination effort by planners, architects, construction firms and local business interests to get the job done. Building a new eco-city – apart from being very expensive, of course – requires a lot of new skills that traditional construction workers just don't have. You also have to consider the sustainability of the materials. It's no good making a zero-energy house if you use enormous amounts of energy producing the concrete and other materials to build it. Each time you come up with an eco-solution, you find that you've created other problems that have to be dealt with.
P: Can we just focus on some of those solutions for a moment? Can you describe to our listeners some of the elements that make an eco-city sustainable?
J: Well, the first thing is the layout of the city. Business districts are placed close to where people live to encourage people to walk to work. Secondly, transportation is electric-powered: electric cars, electric skyway trains, and so on, so a number of clean generation methods are used to produce electricity in a non-polluting way.
P: Such as?
J: One idea is pavements that convert the energy of people's feet walking on them into electrical energy. But wind turbines and solar panels usually provide most of the energy. The key thing is that no extra energy should be imported from outside. That goes for food and water too. Houses collect all the rainwater that falls on or around them and then clean it using UV light so people can use it in the home. Large vertical farms that look a bit like skyscrapers grow vegetables and other crops ...
P: And can I just pick up on something we mentioned earlier and that's the question of waste. How do you deal with that because ...

1.44
Conversation 1
C = Colin, J = Jen
C: I find it incredible that in a big city like this there aren't more leisure facilities. We've got one rather ancient swimming pool, a few tennis courts and a few children's playgrounds.
J: I know what you mean. I think we should get together and write a petition to the local council asking them to do something about it.

Conversation 2
M = Michelle, R = Ruth
M: The problem is that no developer has any incentive to build affordable housing. They all make far more money from luxury homes. Personally, I think it's a disgrace. What's your view?
R: Well, I agree, but I'm just not sure there's much that we, as a council, can do about it. We probably need to consider a completely different solution to the housing problem.

Conversation 3
L = Liz, S = Steve, J = John
L: So, the GFC is asking for a further loan to develop their food co-operative project. What do you think we should do?
S: The way I see it, they have done a good job so far and made all their repayments on time. But it really depends on what they need the money for.
J: Exactly. So, we'll ask them to submit a more detailed proposal. Are we all agreed on that?

Conversation 4
A = Alex, N = Nick
A: Have you seen the plans for that new house across the street? It looks awful: not at all like the other houses round here. If you ask me, we should oppose it.
N: Well, let's not be too hasty. I think it would be better to talk to the new owners first about it. We want to try to keep on good terms with them.

1.45
F = Friend, MA = Model answer
1
F: What do you think of that new shopping mall they are building in the centre of town?
MA: Personally, I think it's horrible. I'd prefer to see more local shops.
2
F: I think that more money should be invested in leisure facilities for young people in the area.
MA: That's right. There's not enough for young people to do.
3
F: The trouble with having a business park out of town is that it encourages people to drive to work. What's your view?
MA: I know what you mean. But if you ask me, it's better than people driving into the city centre.
4
F: Do you think the council should pedestrianise the city centre?
MA: I think that depends on what they plan to do about public transport.
5
F: I find it amazing that no one developed the area around the canal. What they ought to do is make a nice area with shops and restaurants.
MA: I agree. It's an obvious area for development.

Unit 6

2.1
Speaker 1
Let's not pretend that just by staying at home, you're going to relax and switch off. If you're going to get a real break, you need to make a few rules and changes – a few don'ts, if you like. Tell your work that you are going away and you can't be contacted. Don't answer the phone – switch on the answer phone and listen to messages once a day to check that nothing urgent has come in. Change the weekly routine: you don't have to do a weekly shop, for example. Instead, make food shopping something that's fun and nice to do. Shop when you need to; go to the deli, the farmer's market and so on. Don't watch the same old TV programme that you watch each week. Don't do the cleaning – get a cleaner. I don't want to sound prescriptive, but unless you make some rules, you just won't relax properly.

Speaker 2
My idea of a staycation is to pamper myself for a week. I call it my 'home spa week'. I get up late. I go for a walk or a short run, and then I have a massage each day at the local health club. It would be easier not to do things to keep fit, but actually it makes me feel fantastic for the rest of the day. Then I take a late lunch – down by the waterfront usually – and spend the rest of the afternoon reading. Some evenings I spend the time preparing a meal very carefully; other times I go out to a show. I don't think it's extravagant, because I know whatever I do, I'm spending less than I would be if I went away on holiday.

Speaker 3
We had a staycation last year and I just organised loads of exciting things for the family to do every day. I hope I didn't overdo it. I think they enjoyed it. I'm just not one of those people who likes to sit still and do nothing when I'm on holiday. So we went to two theme parks; we went mountain biking in the Brecon hills; we even camped out in the garden one night. I think holidays are all about experiences and we certainly had some of those. We got lost on our bikes one day for about four hours. I tried not to let the children know that I was worried, but I was! Luckily we found the track again before it got dark.

Speaker 4
My advice for a staycation is just to keep it simple. It's an opportunity to enjoy the basic things in life and what nature has to offer. So you really mustn't let modern life dictate what you do too much. Do things with the family – take walks together, make meals for each other, play family games or just chat in the evenings – and don't get involved with anything even vaguely electronic, like computer games or the TV.

2.2
1 In tough economic times, people will try not to spend so much on luxuries and that includes holidays.
2 However, they don't want to go without a holiday altogether, because holidays are an important break from the stresses of work and daily life.
3 You don't have to go abroad to go on holiday. You can have a staycation instead. These have increased in popularity in recent years.
4 I don't think it's a bad trend because it means that people discover more about their own country, and at the same time, they boost the local economy.

2.4
If the saying 'Don't judge a book by its cover' was ever meant for a ship, then it should apply to the *National Geographic Endeavour*. The *Endeavour* was launched in 1966 as a North Sea fishing trawler and is very different from the modern lines of the cruise ships you see today swanning around the Caribbean. It looks more like a working ship, with a number of cranes for launching kayaks and other small boats. In fact, *NG Endeavour* is less of a cruise ship and more of an expedition ship that manages to mix comfort with exploration.

You won't find luxuries such as casinos, room service or in-cabin TVs on the *Endeavour*. Instead, you'll use the ship as a base camp while voyaging to some of the wildest locations on Earth, and you'll find that itineraries are never set in stone. Weather, wildlife and ice conditions always decide the afternoon's plans. Instead of shopping, you'll be kayaking among Antarctic icebergs or waking up at 2 a.m. to a ship's announcement saying that a polar bear has been spotted near the ship.

It's not cheap – fares of $500 to $1,000 a day – but you get value for your money: extraordinary experiences in the most remote regions on earth, a high degree of comfort and a healthy dose of excitement. It's equipped with sophisticated gadgets like the video microscope that magnifies images of sea-life up to 400 times; hydrophones that record whales

singing underwater; and the Zodiacs or inflatable rubber boats that enable you to land just about anywhere.
What else can you expect? Well, the passengers on *NG Endeavour* are mostly well-off, well-educated Americans in their 50s and 60s. At those prices, perhaps that's not surprising. Although there's only one shared dining room, and breakfast and lunch are buffets, the food is surprisingly tasty and varied.

Photographers from the *National Geographic* magazine accompany each voyage, and give passengers advice and instruction on how to take amazing pictures. *NG Endeavour* also employs expert naturalists as guides, who seem as excited as the passengers. Many of them have advanced degrees, all are very knowledgeable. Happily, they are also approachable and enthusiastic. You can get to know them on guided walks on shore, over meals, and in the bar at night.

Throughout the year, *NG Endeavour* sails from one end of the Earth to the other. From June to August, it's usually in Svalbard, way above the Arctic Circle, looking for polar bears. It then makes its way slowly south, through the Mediterranean for expeditions with a more historical and cultural focus, before heading to Antarctica, where it stays from November to March.

2.5

J = Joe, S = Steve

J: Hey, Steve. It's Joe. I'm just calling to say I'll be coming in on the five o'clock train this evening.
S: Fantastic … But I can't pick you up, I'm afraid. I'll be working then.
J: That's OK. I'll just make my way over to you at home – if that's all right.
S: Well, you could do that, but alternatively, since it's going to be a nice evening, why don't we meet up in town – say at Sara's Café down by the seafront?
J: Yeah, all right. That sounds nice. How do I get to Sara's Café?
S: Just hop on any bus from the station and ask the driver for King's Street.
J: OK.
S: Look out for the pier and get off there. Then walk down the front towards the city centre and you'll see the café on your right.
J: OK. If I get held up, I'll call you.
S: Actually, why don't you come and meet me at my office first? It's just as easy.
J: OK, where's that?
S: Well, get off at the same stop and walk in the same direction but turn down Ship Street. Call me when you get there and I'll come out and meet you.

2.6

1 I'd prefer to drive, but the car is behaving strangely.
2 It's not difficult to find, but it's quite a long way from the station.
3 I could come and meet you, but I don't finish work until 6.00 p.m.
4 The bus is cheap, but it makes a lot of stops on the way.
5 You could take a taxi, but it's a very scenic walk.

2.7

F = friend, MA = model answer

1
F: Hi there. I'm coming in on the train tomorrow at two o'clock. What's the best way to get to your house from there?
MA: The easiest thing is to take the bus.
2
F: OK. Is it far?
MA: No, it's only a ten-minute ride.
3
F: Great and how do I know when it's my stop?
MA: Look out for the big shoe factory on your left and it's the next stop after that.
4
F: OK, and what do I do when I get off the bus?
MA: Walk along the road until you see Harbord Road on your left. Turn down there.
5
F: Shall I call you when I get there?
MA: That's a good idea. Then I'll come out and meet you.
6
F: Great. Look, if I get held up, I'll call you. Otherwise, look forward to seeing you tomorrow.
MA: Yes, me too. Have a good trip.

Unit 7

2.9

P = Presenter, E = Expert

P: Even though we wish oil would go on forever, sooner or later it's going to run out. The question is not 'if' but 'when'. A lot of people have talked about peak oil in recent years – the point when oil stocks start to decline. Some people say we've reached this point already; others say it's still fifteen years away. Terry Pritchard, an expert from the oil industry, is here in the studio. Mr Pritchard, what's the truth?
E: I wish I was able to give you a straight answer – but the fact is no one knows. It depends on how you look at it. We passed the peak for oil extracted by conventional methods – that is, drilling a hole into a reservoir 200 metres below the surface of the Earth – in around 2006. But these days, people extract a lot of oil using unconventional means – deep-water drilling and so on. And the peak for that kind of oil is still a few years away. Of course, a lot of people wish that we hadn't started to go down this 'unconventional' route because the new methods are dangerous – the oil spill in the Gulf of Mexico in 2010 is an example.
P: OK, but either way the peak is not far in the future. And the price of oil is going to rise as reserves become smaller. So why hasn't anyone managed to replace oil with something else? I'm sure people would rather have a cheaper and cleaner alternative.
E: If only there was a cheaper, cleaner and more efficient alternative. The problem is transport. You see, petrol is incredibly convenient: it produces a lot of energy, it's easily stored and it can be delivered from a tank to an engine very simply – with just a few pipes. You read a lot about electric and hydrogen vehicles, but these technologies have their drawbacks.
P: Such as?
E: Well, hydrogen has to be stored under very high pressure, so the car becomes a bit like a moving bomb. And electric vehicles have a limited range – around 200 miles maximum.
P: That doesn't sound bad at all.
E: No, but if everyone had electric cars, we'd need a lot of lithium batteries and lithium is also scarce. So it becomes a choice. Would you rather we ran out of oil or lithium?

2.11

The recent discovery of oil in the tar sands of Alberta has put Canada in third place in the world in oil reserves.

However, extracting this oil creates two to four times the quantity of greenhouse gases as conventional methods of extraction.

As a result, Canada has been under a lot of pressure to limit the environmental impact of its new oil industry.

2.12

Speaker 1

In the 1970s, Cancún was just a small fishing village – a few huts on the edge of a mangrove forest. Today that forest is buried and rotting underneath 500 hotels. Only a few inhabitants remember the forest and the seven million tourists that visit each year don't know it ever existed. This place is a classic example of how not to build a tourist resort. Nature is for sale here. The mangroves are not the only victims. The coral reef all along the coast is also slowly being destroyed by all the tourists' pollution. Very little waste water is treated: it's either pumped into the sea or injected into the land, from where in time it returns to the surface. Up to now, conservationists have failed to stop this development or the pollution it's caused.

Speaker 2

The story of the West African giraffe is a conservation success story. A heroic effort on the part of conservationists has saved the giraffe from extinction – from numbers as low as 50 giraffes 20 years ago to over 200 today. The main job was to track the giraffe's movements, since they travel huge distances looking for food. This was done by fitting them with GPS satellite collars – easy with their long necks, you'd think, but actually it's a delicate operation because the giraffes have to be anaesthetised first. Once they knew where the giraffes were going, the conservationists could then begin to educate local people about the dangers facing these wonderful creatures, and to compensate farmers when their land had been damaged by them.

Speaker 3

If you mention the term 'conservation efforts', people tend to think of attempts to save endangered animals, like the tiger; or to protect poor communities from big corporate organisations who are trying to use their land. But in fact, many conservation efforts are small in scale and many have positive outcomes. I'll give you an example: the black poplar tree in Britain. The black poplar is one of Britain's rarest species of tree and its numbers have been declining for decades. That's because much of its natural habitat – the floodplain – has been built on with new housing. Less floodplain means less protection against flooding. So conservationists persuaded local authorities to stop building on the floodplain and reintroduce the trees. As a result, black poplar numbers are rising again.

2.13

1

Globalisation is a force for good. It brings us all closer together. You'll say, 'Yes, it makes us all watch the same TV programmes and want to buy the same brands,' but that's not the point. The point is that it helps us to understand each other better: our differences and our similarities, our hopes and our fears.

2

Sorry, I just don't accept that. All it helps is people in rich countries to have cheaper goods and also goods out of season. To be honest with you, I could live without flowers that are imported from Africa in December or my computer technical support team being based in India.

3

We're approaching this debate all wrong. Globalisation is just a natural economic phenomenon. It gives countries a much bigger market so that they can concentrate on producing the things they're good at producing. Imagine if we had to grow our own coffee in England. That would be nonsense.

4

And that's a silly example. Let me give you another example: people in China making cheap toys for us to give to our children. These people would be much better off making things that were really useful to them. There's no doubt that it's helped the rich countries, but overall globalisation has just increased the gap between the world's rich and poor.

2.14

1 Globalisation may have helped the rich, but it hasn't helped the poor.
2 Globalisation is not something that has been invented; it's a natural phenomenon.
3 I like having things that I can't buy locally, but I don't actually need them.
4 Globalisation doesn't harm poor countries; it helps them.
5 I wish you were right, but the facts show the opposite.

2.15

F = Friend, MA = Model answer

1

F: What do you think about globalisation?
MA: To be honest with you, I think it's probably a good thing.

2

F: But don't you think that it just makes the gap between rich and poor wider?
MA: No, I don't accept that.

3

F: What makes you say that?
MA: Well, take India for example. They have a lot of skilled workers who are making good money working for western companies.

4

F: And what do you think of people who say globalisation's just making us all the same?
MA: That's not the point. The point is whether it's making us all richer and improving our standard of living.

2.18

Globalisation is a force for good. It brings us all closer together. You'll say, 'Yes, it makes us all watch the same TV programmes and want to buy the same brands,' but that's not the point. The point is that it helps us to understand each other better: our differences and our similarities, our hopes and our fears.

Unit 8

2.19

P = Presenter, J = Journalist

P: … that's just one aspect of photojournalism. The question I'd really like to put to you is: When is altering a photo OK and when is it not?
J: Well, … that's a good question. In 1982, *National Geographic* magazine published on its cover a photo of the pyramids in Egypt. In order to fit the tops of the two pyramids onto its cover, photo editors digitally decreased the space between them. People said that this was a manipulation of reality and was wrong. Several years later, an associate editor defended the action. He said that although the magazine had altered the image, they hadn't done anything wrong. He said that he was opposed in general to manipulation of images, but that the cover was a graphic item, not a photo in a news story. He also said that photo editors had always touched up photos, but that this practice was now becoming more sophisticated with tools like Photoshop and Scitex.
P: So he said it was the fault of modern technology that people were altering images?

J: No ... He was saying that the cover of a magazine was more like a piece of advertising, and it had to look aesthetically pleasing to help the magazine sell.
P: You mean the cover has to look good?
J: Yes, that's right. Other editors have used the same argument to alter images for book covers.
P: And what about cases of manipulation in hard news stories – you know, really serious and important ones?
J: That is, of course, a far more serious thing. Again in the 1980s, there was a case with *Picture Week* magazine. The magazine put together two different photos – one of Nancy Reagan, the other of Raisa Gorbachev – put them together in such a way that they appeared to be great friends. This wasn't actually the case and of course people complained, saying that they had been given a false impression.
P: So what's the rule?
J: Well, some people say, 'Don't trust a photo if there's anything important riding on it.' Personally, I think that's going too far. We live now in a world of digitally enhanced visual images and alternative realities. But the public's not stupid – they know that and can make up their own minds about what's real and what's not.

2.21

1 Like many of his fellow professionals, photographer Fritz Hoffman recommends using an analogue camera.
2 A digital camera encourages you to look at the preview before you take a photo, but an analogue camera keeps you in the moment.
3 Hoffman also claims that with a digital camera you need more time to edit the images after they've been taken.
4 That's so that you can make them look like the image as you saw it.

2.23

The difficulty with journalism is trying always to make sure that you give a balanced view, to get your facts right and at the same time tell a good story. *National Geographic* tries to find places where we can marvel at the wonders of nature and places where it thinks that natural ecosystems are in danger.

In the August 2011 issue, the magazine brought the world's attention to such a place, the Great Bear Rainforest in Canada. The main article was a full feature entitled 'The Wildest Place in North America, Land of the Spirit Bear' and described the beauty of the white Kermode Spirit Bear. A smaller article, called 'Pipeline through Paradise', described the building of a gas pipeline through 'Great Bear' country to a gas terminal on the coast at a place called Kitimat. Here huge tanker ships will be loaded up with liquefied natural gas. The article stated that, 'The government has already approved a fleet of liquefied natural gas tankers to call at nearby Kitimat in 2015.'

Strictly speaking, this was factually inaccurate and it upset the company building the pipeline a great deal. Building of the terminal had in fact already begun, and the local government had given its verbal approval to the pipeline. But the company had not received an official licence at the time of publication of the article. Even though it's very probable that a licence will be granted, the journalists and editors in question clearly jumped the gun in order to make their point.

The article highlights the dilemma for journalists. They want to write an interesting article and one that gives definite, not probable, news. They also want to get the story first, before it appears in other newspapers or magazines. The people involved, on the other hand – in this case the company representatives who were interviewed for the article – want **all** the facts to be presented, not only the ones that interest the journalist. They also want any comment to be balanced: in other words, for the same amount of space to be given to their own views as to the journalist's. Ideally, they'd like to have the last word, but of course no journalist should allow that.

2.24

A = Annie, J = Jane
J: Hi Annie.
A: Hi Jane. Did you hear the good news about Patrick? Guess what?
J: What?
A: Well, you know he was doing a comedy routine ...
J: You mean that show that he and his friends took to the Edinburgh Festival.
A: Yes. Well, apparently he was spotted by someone from a big theatrical agency and they want him to sign a contract with them.
J: Really? Who told you about it?
A: Er ... Kate. She reckons that it won't be long before we see him on TV.
J: Hmm ... Well, I'd take that with a pinch of salt if I were you. It could just mean he gets a bit of advertising work or something.
A: No, according to Kate, it's more than that. They talked about him getting acting parts on TV.
J: Really? Well, that'd be fantastic. I heard that it was really difficult to get that kind of work.
A: I think it is, which shows he must have really impressed them. But don't tell anyone just yet. I think he wants to keep quiet about it.
J: Don't worry. I'm not the type to spread gossip. Does the agency take a big fee?
A: It seems that they only take 10% or 15%, supposedly.
J: That sounds all right. Well, that's great news. Thanks for telling me.

2.26

F = Friend, MA = Model answer
1
F: Did you hear the good news about taxes?
MA: Good news about taxes? No, what happened?
2
F: Apparently, the government is going to reduce taxes for all workers.
MA: Really? That doesn't sound very likely. Who told you that?
3
F: Ben told me. It seems that everyone will only pay half the tax they are paying now.
MA: Half? Hmm ... Take no notice of what Ben says.
4
F: Well, maybe he's blown it a bit out of proportion. He said it will be on the news tonight.
MA: OK. Well, I'll watch the news and see.
5
F: What do you reckon is the truth of it?
MA: I reckon that they've reduced taxes by half a percent or something and Ben misunderstood.

Unit 9

2.27

P = Presenter, M = Marjorie Barakowski
P: Ronald Reagan was raised in a small village in Illinois and he graduated from Eureka College, Illinois with a degree in economics and sociology. He worked for a short time as a radio broadcaster in Iowa, and then moved to Los Angeles to follow a career as an actor in films and television. After joining the Republican Party

in 1962, his skills as an orator were noticed and he was persuaded to run for Governor of California. He did a good job as Governor and this led to his nomination for Republican presidential candidate in 1980, which he won. He then went on to become the President of the United States between 1981 and 1989. He took a hard line against communism and his second term of office saw the collapse of the Soviet Union and the beginning of the end of communism in eastern Europe. He was often ridiculed for not being very clever – a second-rate actor, who could only read the lines he was given by his advisors – but he remains one of the most popular American Presidents of the past 50 years. Why? I put that question to political historian Marjorie Barakowski.

M: Ronald Reagan understood the fundamental essence of leadership: that is, that you have to be able to communicate. Reagan always gave the impression that he was listening when he was speaking to you. It was almost as if it didn't matter what his political views were. He made people feel that they mattered. He looked you in the eye, smiled at you, made you feel special. That is a fantastic quality to have.

I'd also have to say that he presided over a time of great economic growth in America. When he came to power, things weren't great for most Americans and he gave them hope. It obviously helped that the economy thrived during his presidency. But, nevertheless, Reagan's style of communication stands out as a model for all leaders. If you can connect with the ordinary person, there's very little you can do wrong.

2.29

1 I guess I was lucky to do a subject that not many other people at college did. I studied plant sciences and after my course, I got a job as a research assistant at the Institute of Botany.

2 It's not easy to be an artist and make a living from it. You are always wondering if it would be better just to get a job with a regular income.

3 I was always told that having good qualifications and the right degree opens doors, but actually it's good communication skills that help you advance in an organisation.

2.30

I = Interviewer, V = Virginia Stanton

I: What are the particular qualities that men and women bring to leadership? Does it in fact make any difference to an organisation if its leader is a man or a woman? I have with me Virginia Stanton, author of *Women who Lead*. Virginia, surely in this day and age it doesn't matter that much, does it, what gender a leader is, as long as they're a good leader?

V: Well, if you say that, you're actually ignoring the differences that a number of studies have identified between male and female leaders.

I: And what are they?

V: Well, some of them will probably surprise you. It's statistically proven that women are a) more adventurous – they're happy to take risks and b) more effective – they focus harder on getting the job done.

I: That is a little surprising, yes.

V: Less surprising perhaps is that they tend to be more sensitive and caring – that is to say, they listen better than men and try to take other people's views into account before making a decision. That's because they seem to care more about their relationships with those around them.

I: And I suppose you're going to say, then, that men are more assertive and dominant – they force their own will on others around them. That's a bit of a stereotype, isn't it?

V: Well, actually, the studies show that women, in fact, are better at insisting on a point – on things being done the way they want them. They tend to be more persuasive than men.

I: I wouldn't have guessed that, I must say.

V: Well, I think the important thing here is that whereas in the past, leaders – male leaders, that is – were more autocratic – 'just do what I tell you to do and don't answer back' – these days you need to be more inclusive and gentler in your dealings with people. It's long been recognised that women, who traditionally have been the ones to organise and manage families or groups of volunteers in charity organisations, have these qualities. More and more, these are qualities that are needed today in the world of business and politics.

2.31

effective sensitive assertive persuasive inclusive

2.33

Speaker 1

Well, I'd be interested to know a bit more about the job, because although I'm very keen on the idea of working with young people – people are always telling me that I'm very good with children – I actually don't have much direct experience of this age group.

Speaker 2

I specialise in canoeing and various other water sports, but I feel comfortable with most outdoor activities really – as long as you're not going to expect me to lead a climbing expedition up a glacier or anything. I haven't done mountaineering. But I have led groups before, so I've got organisational skills.

Speaker 3

I think I'd be very well suited to this job, actually. Although I haven't led expeditions as such, I've been working as a physical education teacher at my local secondary school for the last four years. I'm good at quite a number of sports, in fact. But when I saw your advertisement, I thought, 'This could be just the thing for me.' I'm familiar with your organisation and I really like the fact that you run these activities for kids from poor backgrounds.

2.35

I = Interviewer, MA = Model answer

1

I: So what did you study at university?

MA: I studied media, but I specialised in newspaper journalism.

2

I: And what attracted you to our newspaper?

MA: I want to follow a career in journalism and I'm very interested in local news.

3

I: How do you feel about working to very strict deadlines?

MA: I think I'm good at working under pressure. I had a lot of experience of that at university.

4

I: Have you had any experience of writing for a newspaper before?

MA: Not really, but I think I write well and I'm very keen to learn.

5

I: If you get the job, don't you think you might become bored just dealing with local news stories?

MA: No. I'm serious about wanting to become a professional journalist and this would be a perfect place to start.

Unit 10

2.36

Speaker 1

People who are in favour of teaching your children at home generally argue that the local schools don't stretch children enough, or that they don't recognise their child's individual needs. I'm sure these people mean well, but I think they're missing the point. Interaction with other children from a range of backgrounds – not just your own brothers and sisters – is a key part of learning and you just don't get that if you're stuck in your own house all day.

Speaker 2

Parents often discipline their children for fighting or being unkind to each other, but there's new evidence to suggest that this kind of behaviour may not be a bad thing. Psychologists say that by competing in this way, children are learning valuable social skills. It's common for brothers and sisters to squabble over toys or to compete for attention. They will even continue to do this later in life – fight for their parents' approval, that is – but generally they find a way of working it out so that no one's hurt. That type of negotiation in relationships is important training for later life.

Speaker 3

Where you are in the family clearly has an influence on your behaviour more generally. We're all familiar with eldest children who are organising and bossy types and middle children who feel ignored. Being the baby of our family, I'm particularly interested in youngest child syndrome. Certainly you have to fight more for attention – that's why younger children are often the clowns of the family. Parents tend to let you get away with things that your brothers and sisters didn't. You also have the advantage of learning from your older siblings ... and their mistakes.

Speaker 4

I think far too much attention is paid to how parents should bring up children and far too little to how much other environmental factors affect them. Have you ever watched a two-year-old when another slightly older child comes into the room? They're fascinated. They watch what they do, they try to join in – much more than with an adult. What's more, the elder child will quickly take on the role of teacher or parent, explaining pictures in a book, for example, 'Look. That's a lion! Can you say "lion"?' In a lot of societies, it's quite normal in large families just to leave the children to get on with it. I think parents in the West should do that instead of intervening so much.

2.37

Everything depends on what you see as the future role of your children. In other words, what is it that you are raising them to do?

Do you want them to be good members of society? If so, you will teach them values such as obeying the law, co-operating with others and generally being good citizens.

Or do you want them to be successful individuals? If so, you will help them to be free thinkers and to be independent.

Or is it important that they are good family members? Then you will teach them to respect their elders and to follow family traditions.

2.39

/u:/: blue, fortune, lunar, rude, suit, truce

/ju:/: consume, humanity, humour, menu, used, usually

2.40

Desmond Morris trained originally as a zoologist and in that capacity, he observed the behaviour of many different species of animals. However, his lifelong interest has been human rather than animal behaviour, and unlike the traditional experts in human behaviour – the psychologist, the sociologist and the anthropologist – he is not so interested in what people say, but rather in what they do. In fact, he gives little attention to human speech because he feels that human actions tell us far more about people than anything they might say. Indeed, it is said that in human communication, as much as 90% is non-verbal.

In an interview given some years ago on BBC's Radio 4, Morris gave a fascinating example of this. The non-verbal communication that he described was called 'postural echo' and this is how he explained it. Morris and the presenter were sitting discussing Morris's work in a radio studio. They were both sitting down facing each other across a table. Both had one forearm resting on the table and the other forearm upright with their chin resting on one hand. Both were leaning forward interestedly as they talked to each other. They had adopted what Morris called postural echo: that is to say, because they had a common interest, they were imitating each other's posture. This particular posture I've just described is typical when people are showing interest in what they are hearing.

In another situation, though, such postural echo might be totally inappropriate. The example Morris gave was that of a job interview. Imagine you are being interviewed for a job and the boss who is interviewing you sits back in his chair and puts his feet up on a stool. His posture is showing that he is in a relaxed and dominant position. Your posture, on the other hand, should show that you are in a subordinate position: in other words you should be sitting upright, perhaps leaning forward a little to show interest, with your hands on your lap. If you were to echo his posture, it would send the message that you felt as relaxed as him and he is not hiring another boss – he is looking for a subordinate. At best, you would not get the job; at worst, the boss would find it deeply insulting and end the interview immediately.

2.42

Dowry-giving, the gift of money from one family to another on the occasion of a marriage, is still common in certain parts of the world. It symbolises different things. For example, it can be a sign of wealth and increase social status. It can have a historical and practical meaning: as a rule, in the past, brides did not go out to work, so this was her financial contribution to the marriage. It's customary for a dowry to be given by the bride's family to the groom's family, but it can work the other way around, as in Nigeria, where a small dowry is given by the groom's family.

The engagement ceremony in Nigeria marks the beginning of the wedding celebrations and is an occasion for people to celebrate and have fun before the official ceremony, and also to give gifts to the couple. It takes place on the evening or a couple of nights before the wedding itself. During the party, there's a lot of music, often played by a live band, and dancing. It used to be traditional for money to be thrown at the couple's feet while they danced, but now people usually bring regular wedding gifts. After the party, the groom's family delivers a kind of dowry to the bride's family's house in the form of a gift of traditional clothes and jewellery. It's not the last time the groom has to visit the bride's house. On the night of the wedding, after the reception party is finished, the bride goes back to her own house where she waits until she's claimed by the groom and taken to their new home.

2.44

F = Friend, MA = Model answer

1

F: What does the groom wear on his wedding day?

MA: It's traditional for the groom to wear a morning suit and a top hat, but these days, he can also wear an ordinary suit.

2

F: What symbolic acts are there at the ceremony?

MA: The bride arrives with her father and he then gives her hand to the groom. That symbolises the handing over of his responsibility for her to the groom.

3

F: What happens after the wedding ceremony?

MA: The bride and groom go to a reception, usually in a special car, where they have a big party with all their friends and family.

4

F: What kinds of gifts are given?

MA: Usually people give the couple things that will be useful in their new home: kitchen equipment and so on.

5

F: Is special music played at the reception?

MA: Not really. Once the bride and groom have had their first dance together, everyone usually dances to pop music.

Unit 11

3.1

Dr K. David Harrison believes that language diversity is just as important as bio-diversity. He's part of a *National Geographic* project called 'Enduring Voices', whose aim is to document languages which are little known and in danger of becoming extinct. It's estimated that over half the world's 7,000 languages will disappear by 2050 and so the race is on to trace and record these languages, and also to help keep them alive.

Diversity does not depend on the size of a territory or country. In Bolivia, which only has a population of twelve million, there are 37 different languages, belonging to eighteen language families. This is the same number as the whole of Europe.

Dr Harrison seeks out these language 'hotspots' – places where there is a great diversity of languages spoken and where some are in danger. Studies in the Oklahoma region of the USA succeeded in discovering 26 languages, one of which, Yuchi, had as few as seven speakers. By highlighting this fact, researchers were able to help the community to keep this dying language alive.

Why is this work important? According to Harrison, 'When we lose a language, we lose centuries of human thinking about time, seasons, sea creatures, reindeer, edible flowers, mathematics, landscapes, myths, music ... the unknown and the everyday.' Some ancient cultures managed to build large monuments by which we can remember their achievements, but all cultures express their genius through their languages and stories. We would be shocked if the Great Pyramid at Giza disappeared; we should be equally concerned when we lose a language.

These languages store knowledge which can be of huge benefit to people today. The Yupik language is spoken by the Eskimo peoples of Siberia and Alaska. A book written a few years ago by Yupik elders and scientists in which they described the changing conditions of the ice in the Arctic was able to help other scientists to understand how climate change is affecting the polar ice.

One of the original arguments for globalisation was that it could bring us all closer together. And in some ways this may be true – but that doesn't mean we all have to do the same thing – eat the same food and speak the same language. If anything, globalisation has reminded us how important differences and diversity are. He couldn't save Ubykh – a language spoken near the Black Sea – from extinction, or Kakadu – an Australian aboriginal language, but Harrison and his team aim to save as many languages as they can.

3.2

1 Examples of two languages that have become extinct this century are Munichi – M-U-N-I-C-H-I – from Peru and Wappo – W-A-P-P-O – from the San Francisco area of the USA.

2 David Harrison is a linguist at Swarthmore College (S-W-A-R-T-H-M-O-R-E) in Pennsylvania (P-E-N-N-S-Y-L-V-A-N-I-A).

3 In 2008, the Enduring Voices project found a new language in Arunchal Pradesh (A-R-U-N-C-H-A-L) in India, called Koro, K-O-R-O.

4 Chary is a word from the Siberian language 'Tofa'. Spelt C-H-A-R-Y, it means a four-year-old domesticated reindeer.

5 The longest non-scientific word in the English language is floccinaucinihilipilification, which means the habit of regarding something as unimportant. I'll spell it: F-L-O-C-C-I-N-A-U-C-I-N-I-H-I-L-I-P-I-L-I-F-I-C-A-T-I-O-N.

3.4

1 Meg is a border collie, a smart breed of dog used by farmers because they understand instructions well and they like to be helpful. Their usual job is to round up and direct sheep. You can show Meg a picture of a toy and tell her its name (like a duck or a frisbee), then ask her to go and find it in a room full of toys. Once she has found it once and learned the name, all you have to do the next time is to ask her to fetch the the duck or the frisbee from the room and she will go and find it.

2 Betty is a New Caledonian crow. These animals are pretty inventive tool makers. In the wild, they use sticks, for example, to get insects out of trees. But what they found in the lab was that these birds were able to make tools from materials that they had never used before. Experimenters placed a piece of meat in a little basket and put it in a tube. Betty looked at the problem, then found a straight piece of wire, bent it into the shape of a hook using her beak and lifted the basket from the tube.

3 Maya is a dolphin. I think most people know that dolphins have incredible imitative abilities. They can see an action performed and then repeat it when ordered to. They also seem to understand spoken directions from humans very well. So you can get two of them to leap out of the water and turn a somersault at the same time. But in fact they do these kinds of synchronised tricks in the wild anyway, because they're naturally playful creatures, but no one really understands how they communicate with each other to get the timing so perfect.

4 Kanzi is a Bonobo monkey who has been taught sign language so that he can communicate with humans. One anecdote about his intelligence is that on a walk in the woods, Kanzi indicated that he wanted marshmallows and a fire. He was given the marshmallows and some matches. He found some twigs, broke them into pieces, built a fire, lit it with the matches and then, most amazingly, toasted the marshmallows on a stick over the fire. Bonobos are known for being expressive and good communicators, but even experts who study them were surprised by this behaviour.

5 Psychobird is a western scrub-jay. These birds are known for being pretty mischevious – they play tricks all the time. They're also supposed to be the only non-mammals that plan ahead. They hide food that they're storing up for future use in stores or caches. Their large memories allow them to remember as many as 200 such hiding places. In a lab, Psychobird hid food so carefully that none of the experimenters could work out where she had put it.

3.5

S = Student, L = Lecturer

S: Hi, have you got a minute? I just wanted to ask a bit more about this course.
L: Sure, how can I help?
S: Well, first of all thanks for the interesting lecture. [L: You're welcome – glad you found it interesting …] but there's quite a lot to take in and I don't really have the same background knowledge as some of the other students.
L: Don't worry – I think a lot of people find it difficult at first. Things will become clearer.
S: Well, can you explain what the course is going to be about, because I thought it was going to be about Roman history mainly.
L: Well, it's a mixture of Greek – mainly Hellenistic – and Roman history.
S: Sorry, I didn't catch that word – Helle-something?
L: Hellenistic – Alexander the Great and so on.
S: Oh, yeah … OK. And are you saying that no previous knowledge of ancient history is needed?
L: Well, a little understanding of the geography of the Eastern Mediterranean is very helpful, and if you've heard or read some Greek myths and legends, it helps too.
S: Sorry, I'm not really with you. You mean stories like the war at Troy and so on?
L: Exactly.
S: OK, well could you give me an example of a book I could read now, outside class?
L: Um, you could have a look at some texts by Herodotus. He was a historian of the 5th century BC and his histories read more like good bedtime stories!
S: Did you say Herodotus?
L: That's right, H-E-R-O-D-O-T-U-S.
S: OK, thanks. I'll do that.

3.7

T = Teacher, MA = Model answer

1
T: So you wanted to ask me a question about the exam at the end of this course?
MA: Yes. Can you explain what the exam involves?
2
T: Yes, there's a two-hour written exam and then a short 'viva' afterwards.
MA: Sorry, what do you mean by 'viva'.
3
T: It's a short oral exam to discuss what you have written. They ask you simple questions.
MA: Could you give me an example of the questions?
4
T: Yes, they might ask you to explain your reasons for an argument. But this part only carries a small proportion of the total mark.
MA: Sorry, I'm not really with you.
5
T: What I mean is the viva or oral exam is only 15% of the total marks.
MA: Did you say 15 or 50%?

Unit 12

3.8

How does national character affect economics? Well, let's just consider people's attitude to money at its simplest level. There are basically two types of people – savers and spenders – and we all know people who fit these descriptions. Savers are prudent and careful, never wasteful. Of course they spend money too, but only when they can afford it and only if it's a wise or long-term investment. On the other side, we have the spenders, the more extravagant types. For them, life is too short to worry about saving a little money here or there.

So, can you apply such simple stereotypes on a national scale? During the 2010–2011 global debt crisis, some commentators tried to do exactly that, saying that certain countries had been irresponsible with the money that they had borrowed from banks and governments in more prudent countries. As a result, people in these countries would have to work longer hours, pay more taxes and even accept lower wages if they wanted to receive any more loans.

The question these commentators failed to ask was whether it was irresponsible of the so-called 'prudent countries' to lend the money in the first place. Because when you lend money, you take two risks: you risk perhaps losing the money, but you also risk putting the borrower in a difficult situation. In such a transaction, both parties have a similar motive – to get more money – and so both have a shared responsibility.

To portray one country as a nation of extravagant spenders and another as a nation of prudent savers is too simplistic. What drives economies in most developed or developing countries is the desire to have a better standard of living. And that goes for all of us, spenders and savers alike. For some people it will mean spending money that they don't have at the moment – taking out a loan to get a new car, for example. For others, it will mean saving money to earn interest on it. And in order for the economy to function successfully, we need both types of person, but only as long as they lend and borrow responsibly.

3.9

I think that people often get into debt because they want a lifestyle that they can't really afford.

It's a lifestyle which is sold to them constantly through advertisements, for example on TV and in magazines.

This desire to have a better lifestyle can affect some governments too. They want to improve their citizens' standard of living so that people will vote for them again.

3.11

/ʃ/: wash, abolished, sugar
/ʧ/: watch, cheap, riches
/ʒ/: pleasure, decision, usually
/ʤ/: change, carriage, wages

3.12

I = Interviewer, R = Rick Castro

I: Most of us will be familiar with the concept of barter from our notions of how primitive societies work: you have a chicken I want and I've just made a new hunting spear that you need. So let's do a deal. But is 'barter' as a system of buying and selling goods and services coming back into fashion? With me is Rick Castro of the Barter Society. Rick, is this a serious alternative to current systems of trade or just a romantic notion?

R: The first thing I'd say is that barter never went out of fashion. People have been using barter as a way of exchanging goods for a lot longer than they have been using money and it is, as you've said, a feature of almost every primitive society past and present. But ... it's also very much a feature of the modern economy. People are making bartering arrangements all the time – it's just that conventional economic statistics – GDP figures and so on – don't record it. How could they?
I: Can you give us an example of that?
R: Yes, I can, but firstly we should make an important distinction between direct barter – that's like the example you gave of two people exchanging a chicken for a spear – and then there's what we call 'exchange barter', which is where you belong to a barter group and make more indirect exchanges ...
I: What does that mean?
R: Well, imagine I'm a yoga teacher and you're a tree surgeon. I need to have a tree cut down in my garden and I'm ready to offer you a whole year of yoga classes in return. But you don't want to do yoga. What happens then? Well, if we belong to a barter exchange group, like 'Bartercard' ...
I: 'Bartercard'? You're not serious ...
R: Perfectly serious. If I belong to a group like that, I can sell my yoga classes for 'trade credits'. These can then be spent buying the goods or services of over 75,000 other members – restaurants, sports shops, almost anything. So if you're a member, I can buy your tree surgery services with my credits.
I: Hang on, though. This is just a tax dodge, isn't it? Normally I would have to pay tax on my tree surgery bill, wouldn't I? And you should charge tax on your yoga classes.
R: Of course these exchanges are liable to tax – at least that's the law in most developed countries.
I: So what's the advantage then? I'm trying hard to see one. Why not just use money?
R: Well, because if you belong to a group like that, it gives you access to a new market – a big circle of new contacts who will potentially become regular customers and ... possibly some of them your friends too!

3.13

A = Client, B = Caterer

A: So there'll be about 60 of us. We want some food but, to be honest, nothing too fancy. I suspect a lot of people will be going home and having supper later anyway.
B: OK, so what did you have in mind? A few canapés, some sandwiches?
A: Well, I was hoping we could have something a bit more exciting than sandwiches.
B: Perhaps if we prepared some sushi, some smoked salmon, a few samosas ...?
A: Yes, that would be much more like it. Is that going to be very pricey?
B: About £10 per person.
A: Mmm ... that's quite a lot, but let's face it, it is an important occasion. You know, it's a leaving party for someone who's been working with us for 37 years, so we don't want it looking cheap.
B: I think that's a good way to look at it. If I were in your shoes, I'd like to put on an event that people would remember. By the way, the £10 also includes the waiting staff for two hours.
A: Oh, we don't need that. We can just help ourselves. Would that reduce the price a bit, then?
B: No, I'm sorry. You have to appreciate that we have to come and set it all up and take it away anyway, so we might as well serve it while we're there.
A: I see. Well, the key thing for us is that it's a nice relaxing event, so we'll go with that, I guess.
B: Great. Just let me know exact numbers when you have them.

3.15

C = Caterer, MA = Model answer

1
C: So what kind of food did you have in mind? Some sandwiches?
MA: I was hoping we could have some hot food too.
2
C: OK. We could provide a few hot pastries as well. How does that sound?
MA: Yes, that would be great.
3
C: That would be about £10 per person.
MA: That's quite a lot. Could you move a bit on that price?
4
C: Sorry. You have to appreciate it's a lot of work for us. We could do it more cheaply but the food would be much more basic.
MA: No. The key thing for us is that it's nice food.
5
C: Well, if I were in your shoes, I would go for the more expensive menu.
MA: I suppose you're right. OK then. We'll do that.

IELTs practice test

3.16

Presenter: In this test you'll hear a number of different recordings and you'll have to answer questions on what you hear. There will be time for you to read the instructions and questions and you will have a chance to check your answers. The recording will be played once only. The test is in four sections.

Now turn to section one on page 100 of your book. You will hear a student called Martin telling his friend about a careers day which is being held in the city where they are studying. First you have some time to look at questions 1 to 5. You will see that there is also an example which has been done for you.

Now we shall begin. You should answer the questions as you listen, because you will not hear the recording a second time. Listen carefully and answer questions 1 to 5.

Woman: Hi, Martin. Did you hear about the careers day that the college is holding? My tutor was just talking about it.

Martin: Yeah, apparently there's something on the notice board about it, or so my flatmate was saying.

Woman: Well, it's probably this leaflet he saw pinned up there. Look, it's got all the details.

Martin: Great. Is it being held in the college then? I heard they were going to hire space in the Town Hall.

Woman: Really? I think you must be thinking of some other event. Our college is actually sharing the day with the technical university, and they're putting the day on at their campus. It's going to be outside in the grounds if the weather's nice.

Martin: Look, it goes on all day from ten till five. I wouldn't want to hang around that long though, just the morning or the afternoon would suit me fine. I start getting bored after a couple of hours at these things.

Woman: Well, look at the programme of talks – it'll help you decide which.

Martin: Anyway, there's a website with all the talks on, so it doesn't matter if you miss some of them.

Woman: Well, the event is free to students enrolled at the college, but the website isn't: you'd have to sign up like anybody else, and there's a monthly fee. But then you do see stuff from other similar events around the country too.

Martin: Sounds good. There are some sessions on in the lunchtime too. Look. And it's not the usual talks by old students or videos about voluntary work in other countries either. You can get tips on how to put a CV together or go to a seminar led by one of the big recruitment agencies.

Woman: Right. My careers advisor was recommending those when I met her for my one-to-one advice session the other day.

Martin: Should be good then.

Presenter: Before you listen to the rest of the conversation, you have some time to read questions 6 to 10.

Now listen and answer questions 6 to 10.

Martin: So what are the main talks on the programme, then?

Woman: Well, each faculty's put up one speaker. Our college in the morning and the technical university in the afternoon. But the speakers aren't only talking about stuff relevant to those subjects.

Martin: Sure. So let's see. It starts at ten and the Law faculty is putting up Professor Jaynes.

Woman: The famous judge?

Martin: No, you're thinking of James. This is Jaynes, J . A . Y . N . E . S. And he's talking about contracts of employment.

Woman: Oh right. Could be interesting though.

Martin: Maybe. But eleven o'clock you've got Professor Smith talking about internships – that should be more interesting. She lectures in accountancy, apparently. So which faculty's that? Economics?

Woman: Business Studies actually.

Martin: Oh yes, of course. Then Dr Wentworth is representing the Languages faculty at eleven. I heard her give a really good talk on cross-cultural misunderstandings last term – you know gestures and stuff you can get wrong – it was brilliant. But this time, she's doing technical translations.

Woman: Oh right. Yeah, she's a good speaker.

Martin: Then after lunch, there's Dr Shah from the Engineering faculty. It says here he's an expert in computer modelling, but he's going to be talking about openings in the construction industry.

Woman: Shame, I'd rather hear about the models.

Martin: Me too. Then there's Dr Bellucci from Sports Science – she's doing something on the Olympic Games which should be interesting – all the different jobs from different disciplines that are involved.

Woman: Right. And then it's our old friend Dr Fulton doing interview techniques. He's working in the Geology department at the technical university now, and they've put him up for this. Though when he was here, he was in the faculty of Geography.

Martin: Still he's a great speaker – always gets a laugh.

Woman: So what do you think ...

Presenter: Now turn to Section 2 on page 102 of your book. You will hear some information about Jodrell Bank, a famous radio telescope, which is part of the University of Manchester. First you have some time to look at questions 11 to 14.

Now listen and answer questions 11 to 14.

Man: Good evening. I'm here to tell you about the Jodrell Bank Observatory, which has been a world leader in radio astronomy since the second half of the twentieth century. The site is part of the University of Manchester and there's also an arboretum with over 2,500 rare trees. A visitor centre provides information about both the famous radio telescope and the trees.

The giant Lovell Telescope that stands on the site is an internationally renowned and awe-inspiring landmark. This is a radio telescope so visitors cannot look through it directly. The observatory buildings are also still in use for operating the telescope so are not usually open to the public. But the visitor centre provides a good view of the telescope and visitors can walk along a pathway not far from the base, where they will find plenty of notices providing information about the history of the telescope and how it works. The centre also provides opportunities to meet the scientists who work at the Observatory.

The visitor centre also provides activities for visitors of all ages. Admission prices at the centre vary according to the type of ticket and the season in which the visit is made. For example, an adult single ticket would cost £6.50 in the summer months and £5.50 at other times of year, whereas a family ticket would cost either £24 or £20. An annual ticket is available for individuals at £19.50 and for families at £60. Concessionary tickets are available at all times for children, students and retired people.

In terms of facilities available at the visitor centre, these are divided between two buildings: the Planet Pavilion, where you'll find the entrance as well as the glass-walled café with outside terrace – you get amazing views of the telescope from there. There's also a gift shop and a small exhibition space where visitors can learn about the planets. The second building is the Space Pavilion, which is the main exhibition area. Here visitors can find answers to the wonders of the universe, listen to the sound of the Big Bang and explore the universe using hands-on activities. As many returning visitors are aware, our planetarium was demolished in 2003, along with the old visitor centre. But we are looking to secure funding to restore this feature in the not-too-distant future.

Presenter: Before you hear the rest of the presentation, you have some time to look at questions 15 to 20.

Now listen and answer questions 15 to 20.

Man: Next, a bit about the history of the telescope. It's named after Sir Bernard Lovell, who was a pioneer in the study of astrophysics in the twentieth century. The site itself, which is about fifteen miles south of the other university buildings in Manchester, first came into the university's possession in 1939. It wasn't the Astrophysics department that bought it, though, but the Botany department who were looking for a place to cultivate wild plants. In 1945, Bernard Lovell was given some equipment to use in his work, including a radar. But because of electrical interference from trams passing the university buildings, it didn't work properly in central Manchester, so he asked to move it to Jodrell Bank instead. It was installed just in time to observe a meteor shower that was visible that year.

Over the next few years, Lovell installed other equipment on the site, including an aerial on a searchlight mount in 1946, and in 1947, the 218-foot Transit Telescope – at the time the largest in the world. This telescope was superseded by a larger and more up-to-date model in 1957. This was named the Mark One Telescope, later upgraded and eventually renamed the Lovell Telescope in honour of Sir Bernard. This telescope became famous in the 1960s for tracking manned and unmanned space missions, as well as providing information about astronomy itself. And the telescope remains a world leader in this field.

Further developments followed in the 1960s and 1970s, including a teaching telescope for use by undergraduates, and the creation of the arboretum in 1972. This features national collections of various rare trees and other plants as well as a scale model of the solar system.

More recent developments at the site have included the opening of a new Discovery Centre in 2011, an event which coincided with a decision to place Jodrell Bank on the UK shortlist for consideration as a site with World Heritage status. In July that year the site also hosted a rock concert called 'Live from Jodrell Bank'. These are excellent examples of how the scientists at Jodrell Bank have always worked hard to engage with the wider community and increase the impact of their science.

Presenter: Now turn to Section 3 on page 103 of your book. You will hear an interview with a medical student called Damian, who is talking about his elective, a period of work experience he did overseas as part of his degree course. First you have some time to look at questions 21 to 24.

Now listen and answer questions 21 to 24.

Woman: Hi, Damian.

Damian: Hi.

Woman: Thanks for coming to talk to college radio about your elective. Now that's a period of work experience in a hospital you do in your final year as a medical student, isn't it?

Damian: That's right. The idea is that being a doctor is about understanding the psycho-social factors involved in each patient, as well as the medical ones. You do an elective in a speciality, to explore it in greater breadth and depth, and that's especially interesting when the placement's abroad.

Woman: So is it a sort of working holiday really?

Damian: No. I wouldn't say that. But electives do also give you the opportunity to travel and have fun. How you balance these two aspects is up to you. Whilst in Belize, I learnt to scuba dive, climbed Mayan ruins and explored the jungle, not something you can say about every medical placement!

Woman: And it's up to you to organise the whole thing, isn't it?

Damian: That's right. Many students have problems when it comes to organising an elective. For some it's the first time they've travelled alone or the first experience of being exposed to different cultures. I was cool with all that, but it's important to choose your speciality well. I had no idea where I wanted to go because I hadn't even chosen a speciality, so that made it tough.

Woman: Do you have to spend the whole period in one place, or can you split it up?

Damian: You can choose. I chose to divide mine into a six-week placement abroad and a two-week placement at home in the UK. Many people would argue that a two-week placement doesn't give you enough time to fit into a team and gain relevant experience, and I'd go along with that. With the benefit of hindsight, I'd have done better with a straight four-week split.

Woman: And where can you go for help with these decisions?

Damian: Well, many companies will organise elective placements for you, as well as providing cover and support ... at a price! But there are lots of companies out there, and I've heard that if you're willing to hunt around, you can find some reasonably priced deals. It's always worth asking round though. If you can talk to people about companies they've used, you can check whether those companies are any good or not. That's how I found the one I went with and I've no complaints.

Presenter: Before you hear the rest of the conversation, you have some time to look at questions 25 to 30.

Now listen and answer questions 25 to 30.

Woman: So Damian, tell us about your placement in Belize.

Damian: Well, having been undecided for a long time between specialising in surgery or emergency medicine, I went for emergency, because I thought it would give me a broader experience than surgery would. My first choice of country would've been Jamaica, but they only had places for dermatology and obstetrics, so that's how Belize came up. I'd never really heard of the country before.

Woman: And was it a company that helped you?

Damian: Yes, they provided photos of medical and non-medical facilities in a couple of different countries in the Caribbean and Central America. In the end, it wasn't the photos of the hospital, but those of the beach that drew me to Belize – perhaps I shouldn't admit to that!

Woman: So tell us a bit about working there.

Damian: The health system in Belize is a mixed one of both public and private. The government subsidises a significant proportion of health care for the average Belizean, although there's a limited number of hospitals with in-patient facilities. Belize has an area of 22,000 square kilometres with only 300,000 people spread sparsely around it, and a big town is one with about 20,000 inhabitants. It means that a significant percentage of the population is rural based and nowhere near a free national hospital.

Woman: Right.

Damian: I was one of three British students placed by the company: the two others were in the south of the country and I think they had a different experience, but up in the north where I was, the biggest frustration was that despite Belize being an English-speaking country, the default language was Spanish, because a lot of the doctors working there are actually Cuban. I speak French, but not Spanish, so when consultations weren't in English, I needed the doctor to explain what had been said.

Woman: Would you go to Belize again?

Damian: Yes. And people do sometimes get jobs in the places they've been to on electives. But next time I wouldn't go with the idea of being a hospital doctor, I'd rather think of teaching the staff. But I think I could've made better use of my clinical experience if I'd learned basic Spanish – so that would be a priority before I went back.

Woman: Damian. Thanks.

Presenter: Now turn to Section 4 on page 104 of your book. You will hear a student giving a presentation about the Antiguan Racer Snake, a rare species living on a Caribbean island. First you have some time to look at questions 31 to 35.

Now listen and answer questions 31 to 35.

Woman: In my presentation today I want to talk about the rarest snake in the world – the Antiguan Racer Snake – an animal that has been rescued from the brink of extinction by the efforts of conservationists.

The snake is one of the racer snake family that is found in various regions across the Americas. It's a small harmless snake that grows to around one metre, with the female being slightly longer than the male.

Many of the racer snakes found in the Caribbean region, and especially those in the southern states of the USA, are black in colour, whereas the Antiguan racer is lighter. The male is closer in colouring to the black racers, being a dark brown, whilst the female is distinguishable by its silver-grey skin.

The Antiguan racer is found in various habitats, including sandy beaches and rocky ridges, but has a preference for dense undergrowth, which is one of the reasons why it's relatively rarely seen.

In terms of diet, the Antiguan racer is very choosy. Other racer snakes feed on small mammals and amphibians such as frogs, but the Antiguan sub-species tends to rely on lizards as its main source of food. Maybe this is one of the reasons why it's an endangered species, although there is little evidence that its prey has ever been in short supply.

Presenter: Before you hear the rest of the presentation, you have some time to look at questions 36 to 40.

Now listen and answer questions 36 to 40.

Woman: By the end of the twentieth century, it was feared that the Antiguan racer, which was once common on the large island of Antigua after which it's named, had indeed become extinct. And this was probably the case. The snake had once been common on the neighbouring island of Barbuda too, but hadn't survived the human development of these large islands. But the local inhabitants were convinced that the snakes might be surviving on one of the smaller islands off the Antiguan coast, such as Rabbit Island or Crump Island, or on Bird Island – the place where one was eventually spotted in 1995.

The tiny island was uninhabited and looked after by the Antiguan Forestry Unit, which was keen for scientists to establish how many snakes might be living there. They commissioned a six-week survey, to be carried out by one of the conservationists who had made the discovery, Mark Day, who later went on to work for the conservation body, Fauna and Flora International.

What was established by his work was that the small island, only measuring some 18,000 square metres, was supporting a racer population of around 100 individuals. The rarest snake in the world was alive and well, but seriously endangered. In 1996, a conservation project was set up to ensure its survival.

And with the current population standing at around 500 snakes, this project has been hailed a success. A captive breeding programme has been effective in increasing numbers, even though it was adversely affected by disease at first. Reintroduction to other nearby islands, and to the mainland of Antigua, has meant eradicating the rats that had decimated the snake population in the twentieth century – a programme that has worked, although the snake's habitat does remain vulnerable to hurricane damage. Now that the species is officially protected, there are unlikely to be further incursions of tourist development into its natural habitat, another cause of its earlier decline. The right kind of habitat is not found over a wide area, though, and this will eventually limit the extent of the snake population. So before I go on to ...

Answer key

Unit 1

1a (pages 4 and 5)

1
b

2
1b 2b 3b 4c 5a 6a

3
1 truth 2 strength 3 warmth 4 length 5 depth

4
1 is dying out, you are trying, France is changing
2 we work with, we chat to, they reserve real intimacy
3 friendships have lost, you have ever visited
4 have been declining

5
1 have you spent *or* have you been spending
2 Do you consider
3 do you have
4 is increasing *or* has increased
5 Have you made
6 have you known
7 do you see
8 do you look for

6
1 intimate, close, strong 2 strong 3 close, closest, true
4 complete 5 casual

7
1 student 2 companion 3 acquaintance 4 flat
5 blood 6 passing

8
1 travel companion
2 odd couple
3 mutual respect
4 fellow students
5 close relative

9
1 out with 2 up with 3 on 4 round 5 by 6 up with
7 up 8 for

1b (pages 6 and 7)

1
1 T 2 F 3 T 4 F 5 T 6 F

2
1 rate 2 boom; retirement 3 diet 4 lifestyle
5 expectancy 6 vaccinations

3
1 are being forced
2 has been raised
3 isn't considered
4 is being encouraged
5 are reduced
6 hasn't been welcomed

4
1 is known
2 are obliged
3 have been educated
4 has been made
5 are also given *or* have also been given
6 is now outnumbered

5
1 is rising 2 is growing 3 has not been received
4 have gone 5 are obliged 6 are being encouraged

6a
1 are given 2 have been made 3 is being discussed
4 has not yet been found 5 is considered 6 are expected

6b
1 W 2 W 3 S 4 W 5 S 6 W

7
1 I think my parents' generation has been quite lucky.
2 My parents worked hard all their lives, but they both retired when they were 60 and they've been given good pensions. So now they can relax and enjoy themselves.
3 They've said that they don't want to be a burden on us, and that we children aren't expected to look after them when they get old.
4 Considering that my husband and I are now being asked to work until we are 68, I'm glad they said that.

1c (page 8)

1
c

2
1 F 2 T 3 T 4 T 5 F 6 T 7 F 8 F

3
1 a 2 a 3 c 4 b 5 b 6 c

4a
1 dynamic 2 fantastic 3 economics 4 generation
5 restriction 6 tradition
Rule: The penultimate syllable is always stressed.

4b
specific italics terrific scientific characteristic
impression relation interruption transformation
comprehension

1d (page 9)

1
1 into 2 – 3 to 4 under 5 – 6 of 7 on 8 – 9 in
10 with

2
1 PPS 2 PPC 3 PPS 4 PPC

3
a present perfect continuous
b present perfect simple

4
1 been wondering 2 been working 3 decided
4 been helping 5 finished 6 lost

5
a Fancy bumping into you here
b What a nice surprise
c it obviously suits you
d how's it all going with you
e Do give her my best regards
f great to see you
g Good luck with the job

6
1 E 2 F 3 E 4 E 5 F 6 E

7
Students' own answers.

1e (page 10)

1
1 g 2 c 3 f 4 e 5 a 6 d 7 b

2
1 How are you **getting on**: doing
2 when you **get** a moment to write: have
3 you're able to **get by**: manage
4 I **got** a letter: received
5 I'm trying not to **get** too excited: become
6 to **get** a job: obtain
7 Sarah is going to **get** married: be

3
1 understand 2 put down 3 bought 4 arrive at *or* reach
5 take *or* catch 6 recover from 7 won 8 find *or* bring *or* fetch

4
1 received *or* got 2 am 3 arrived *or* got 4 sounds
5 have had *or* have been having 6 were *or* got
7 hope 8 have recovered
9 hasn't become *or* hasn't got / doesn't become *or* doesn't get
10 sounds 11 don't think 12 have ever experienced
13 has happened 14 am trying *or* have tried *or* have been trying 15 haven't been 16 find *or* get 17 helped *or* has helped *or* has been helping 18 don't really understand *or* don't really get

Wordbuilding / Learning skills / Check! (page 11)

1
-ful: respectful, helpful, playful
-ish: foolish, childish, selfish
-ive: sensitive, conservative, decisive
-ous: studious, humorous, industrious
-ent/-ant: dependent, different, dominant
-al: entrepreneurial, industrial, intellectual, practical
-ing: caring, controlling, dominating, loving

2
Possible answers:
1 dependent 2 caring/sensitive 3 conservative
4 dominant 5 practical 6 intellectual/studious
7 humorous 8 entrepreunerial 9 industrious

3
1 decisively 2 take 3 indecisive 4 conclusion

4
Students' own answers.

5
1 b 2 c 3 a 4 c 5 c

Unit 2

2a (pages 12 and 13)

1
1 They travel for hundreds of miles to breed.
2 The struggle between life and death.

2
1 have chicks 2 their young 3 dramatic
4 predictable 5 in such hard conditions

3
1 to shoot 2 inspired 3 documentary *or* drama
4 to anticipate 5 struck (me)

4
1 I have also worked as a cameraman.
2 I spent 14 months at the French scientific centre in Antarctica. *and* I helped to shoot another film in 1995.
3 They have never experienced any form of colonisation, so they're not scared of humans. *and* The penguins have learned to live where no other creature can.

5
1 have met 2 have spent 3 have always felt 4 got
5 encountered 6 adapted 7 learned 8 has visited
9 didn't run 10 did

6
1 director 2 sentimental 3 gripping 4 touching 5 cast
6 location 7 accurate 8 storyline 9 audience 10 scenes

7
There is a silent 'l' in the following words: talk, could, calf, folk, calm

8
1 setting for; thought-provoking book
2 characters are you and me and every other typical passenger
3 book is based on conversations that the author had
4 The idea behind it; can portray modern civilisation

2b (pages 14 and 15)

1
b

2
1 a 2 c 3 c 4 b 5 a

3
1 a 2 b 3 b 4 a 5 c 6 b

4
1 drove 2 made 3 arrived 4 had fallen 5 climbed
6 had gone 7 were hanging 8 hadn't told 9 stood
10 had crushed *or* was crushing 11 waited
12 had already decided

5
1 b 2 a 3 c

6
1 hadn't 2 are 3 isn't 4 was 5 weren't 6 was 7 had
8 haven't

7a
The tenses used to describe the film are: present simple, present continuous and present perfect.

7b
1 gives 2 begin 3 reaches *or* has reached
4 grow *or* are growing 5 are getting

2c (page 16)

1
1 T 2 F 3 T 4 T 5 F 6 F

2
1 children; adults 2 fairy tale 3 sadness 4 moved
5 moral lessons

3
1 an elegant 2 watches closely 3 a little swallow stops off with him 4 asks 5 people 6 days 7 catches cold
8 destroy

4
1 c 2 b 3 d 4 a

5
1 kept you from *or* have kept you from
2 kept an eye on
3 keep him company
4 keep track of
5 kept back
6 keep a secret

2d (page 17)

1
1 tore 2 broke 3 stuck 4 made 5 froze 6 burst

2
a What a
b That was
c How *or* That was
d How *or* That was
e What
f How
g Poor
h What *or* That must have been
i How *or* That must have been
j What *or* That must have been

Possible answers:
1 a *or* c 2 a *or* j 3 a *or* c *or* i 4 c 5 a 6 a *or* j

3
1 Hannah's passport was out-of-date.
2 She went to the passport office in London to get a new passport.
3 Very stressed.

4
1 d 2 b 3 f 4 a 5 e 6 c

6
Students' own answers.

2e (page 18)

1a
whispered, replied anxiously, moaned, muttered, cried

1b
1 c 2 b 3 g 4 d 5 e 6 a 7 f

2a
a T b T c T d T

2b
'I don't think this is going to work,' Christopher sighed. 'We've been trying to build this canoe for three days and it still looks like a lump of wood. The wood's too hard,' he added. 'Actually, Christopher,' said Jen encouragingly, 'we are making some progress. What we really need to do is find some better tools.' Just then Tom screamed, 'I've got it! Instead of using our penknives directly on the wood, why don't we make some better tools using our knives?'

3
Model answer:
'Look out,' screamed Fergus, 'I think he's angry now.' The two friends edged nervously backwards as the snake turned its head to face them. Josh had thrown a large rock at it, hoping that this would frighten it, but it seemed that it had had the opposite effect. Now Josh was looking around for something else to hit the snake with. 'Where's a stick when you need one?' he muttered. 'Too late for that,' said Fergus. 'Let's get out of here.' And with that, he leaped towards the trees and started running.

Wordbuilding / Learning skills / Check! (page 19)

1
an author – a novelist
an audience – viewers
a blockbuster – a best-seller
a cinema – a multiplex
to edit – to cut
a film – a movie
a hero – a heroine
to publish – to release
a remake – a re-release
a sequel – a follow-up

2
1 an author *or* a novelist 2 a heroine 3 viewers
4 a best-seller 5 to release 6 to cut 7 a sequel *or* follow-up
8 a multiplex 9 a re-release 10 a movie

3
1 b 2 a 3 a 4 b 5 b 6 a

4, 5 and 6
Students' own answers.

7
1
a a documentary
b a children's story *or* fairy tale
c a book-film adaptation

2
a film director *or* producer
b author *or* writer
c photographer

3
a shave
b stroke
c stretch

Unit 3

3a (pages 20 and 21)

1
c

2
1 standard of living 2 increase 3 more than *or* faster than
4 (two) children 5 one billion 6 three ways *or* three schools of thought *or* three alternatives

3
Greater: rise, boost, grow, increase, raise, peak
Smaller: dwindle, deplete, decrease, fall, lessen, reduce

4
1 reduce 2 rise *or* increase *or* grow 3 decrease *or* fall
4 reduce *or* lessen 5 increase *or* raise *or* boost 6 increase

5
1 will have; will be
2 are going to rely
3 I'll tell; I will be; doesn't start
4 won't solve; share
5 is going to save
6 I'm going; begins

6
1 Are you going *or* Are you going to go
2 are you getting *or* are you going to get
3 'll probably drive *or* am probably going to drive
4 'll go
5 'll give
6 are you leaving *or* are you going to leave
7 starts
8 will finish *or* will be finished

7
1 etcetera 2 contributed 3 lot 4 fifteen 5 years
6 powerful 7 motives 8 meet 9 secretly 10 Manhattan

3b Smart technology (pages 22 and 23)

1
Items mentioned: kitchen gadgets, water use, sound-proofing, visual media, lighting

2
1 a 2 b 3 c 4 c 5 c 6 b

3
1 b 2 g 3 a 4 f 5 h 6 c 7 e 8 d

4
1 will be hearing 2 will be making 3 will all be using
4 will have become 5 will be using 6 will be cleaning
7 will be installing 8 will have become 9 will be launching

5
1 will be doing 2 will be cleaning 3 will have developed
4 will be doing 5 will have been 6 won't have acquired

6
1 information age, information overload, information technology
2 data security, data storage
3 computer games, computer graphics, computer programmer

7
1 data security 2 information age 3 computer graphics 4 data storage 5 information overload

8
1 The weekday edition of *The New York Times* contains more information than the average person in 17th-century England learned in a lifetime.
2 Around a thousand books are published internationally every day and the total of all printed knowledge doubles every five years.
3 More information has been published in the last 30 years than in the previous 5,000.

3c (page 24)

1
1 b 2 c 3 c 4 b

2
1 2007; 6000 2 99.9% 3 15 5 700 5 30 6 2010

3
1 works 2 provides 3 contains 4 lasts 5 weighs
6 costs 7 run

4a
1 /ɪ/ 2 /ɪ/ 3 /aɪ/ 4 /ɪ/ 5 /aɪ/

5
1 neat 2 appropriate 3 consuming 4 handy
5 cutting 6 fix

3d (page 25)

1
1 sort 2 format 3 undo 4 copy 5 select 6 highlight
7 open 8 search 9 attach 10 paste 11 save 12 cut

2
1 He is having trouble sending the document. *or* He's trying to attach a document to an email, but he can't.
2 1 Compress the photos; 2 Divide the document into three or four separate documents.
3 It reduces the quality of the photos.

3
1 give 2 hand 3 trouble 4 exactly 5 trying 6 Let
7 look 8 trouble 9 can 10 involve 11 show 12 trick
13 see 14 else 15 tried 16 try 17 works 18 free

4
The two verbs which do not fit the stress pattern are: highlight and open

5
Students' own answers.

3e (page 26)

1
1 Please could I bring your memory stick back on my way home from work tonight?
2 Do you happen to know where I can find a battery charger for my old phone?
3 Could you please send me a brochure for your air conditioning units?
4 Do you know the phone number for Apricot Computers (please)?
5 Please can/could you advise me how to download photos from my X306 camera?
6 Would you be able to reduce the price?
7 Would you mind coming over and fixing my internet connection?
8 Please could you tell me what number I should call to get technical advice?

2
1 depth 2 question 3 business 4 date 5 order
6 way 7 interest 8 luck

3
1 f 2 d 3 g 4 c 5 h 6 b 7 a 8 e

4
Model answer:

Hi Jim

I hope all is well with you. I tried to call you earlier, but I couldn't get any answer. I wonder if you could do me a favour. My computer keeps crashing and I think it may have the same virus that yours had a few weeks ago. Would you mind emailing me the instructions about how to remove the virus to my work email? Then I can print them and try to see if it works. Alternatively, could you call me some time? I'll be at home most evenings this week.

Many thanks

Sam

Wordbuilding / Learning skills / Check! (page 27)

1
1 biodegradable, biodiversity
2 hypermarket, hypersensitive
3 megabyte, megastar
4 microchip, microwave
5 semi-conscious, semi-detached
6 ultrasonic, ultraviolet

2
1 hypermarket 2 microwave 3 megabyte
4 biodiversity 5 microchip 6 semi-detached
7 hypersensitive 8 ultraviolet 9 ultrasound
10 megastar 11 biodegradable 12 semi-conscious

3
address book
battery life
credit card
data protection
information technology
news story
repair manual
travel advice

4
Students' own answers.

5
1 gadget 2 lazy 3 overload 4 breakthrough
5 appropriate 6 luck
Word: global

Unit 4

4a (pages 28 and 29)

1
1 show, act 2 gig, venue, band 3 exhibition, gallery
4 company, performance, theatre 5 play, musical

2
1 Batman Live, This is Design
2 The Alternative Village Fete, Notting Hill Carnival
3 The Alternative Village Fete, Notting Hill Carnival
4 The Alternative Village Fete
5 The Floating Cinema
6 Notting Hill Carnival
7 Batman Live
8 The Alternative Village Fete

3
1 communal 2 float 3 eye candy 4 mundane
5 workshop

4
1 number 2 no 3 several/some 4 plenty/loads/lots
5 any 6 few

5
1 a little 2 enough 3 a lot of; A large number of
4 plenty of; no 5 a lack of 6 many 7 hardly any
8 a bit of

4b (pages 30 and 31)

1
1 portrait 2 grafitti 3 installation 4 sketch
5 sculpture 6 landscape 7 still life

2
1 In the first photo, the graffiti has been drawn on public walls. In the second photo, the graffiti is part of a piece of artwork.
2 Students' own answers.

3
1 A graffiti artist was convicted of vandalism.
2 Handy thought it was outrageous.
3 When the owner of a property doesn't like it or want it on their property. *or* When it's criminal damage.

4
1 c 2 b 3 c 4 c 5 a 6 a

5
1 person who was invited.
2 method works.
3 anyone came to the opening night.
4 our money.
5 countries have their own laws and rules.
6 world is waiting to see what will happen.

6
1 each; all 2 no 3 both 4 any 5 Every 6 no
7 whole 8 Either *or* Any

7
1 no 2 all the 3 the whole 4 each 5 Both

8
1 The message was clear: is this how far we have come since the Stone Age?
2 Often it carries a political or social message, but in an amusing way that ordinary people can relate to.
3 Despite not calling himself an artist, his work has been shown in galleries and has sold for thousands of dollars.
4 Banksy, who is based in the UK, is perhaps the world's best-known graffiti artist.
5 Banksy loves to surprise. In 2005, a picture showing a primitive human being pushing a shopping cart appeared in the British Museum.

The correct order is: 4, 3, 2, 5, 1

4c (page 32)

1
1 country music 2 dance music 3 (punk) rock 4 hip-hop

2
Suggested answers:
a 3 b 1 c 1 d 4 e 2 f 2

3
1 Country; real
2 influences
3 teenagers; rock
4 sounds; technology

4
1 be connected to 2 escape 3 seem true 4 discover
5 think of 6 (not) be important

5
1 b 2 a 3 b 4 d 5 c 6 a

6
1 c 2 b 3 a 4 d

4d (page 33)

1
1 the Amazon River 2 He likes the presenter.

2
1 X 2 X 3 X

3
1 kind of thing 2 feel particularly inspired 3 a big fan of
4 got on my nerves 5 listen to him 6 a bit tired of

4b
1 I can listen to Bach all day.
2 Documentaries don't really do anything for me.
3 I'm not really into TV.
4 I'm not particularly keen on the presenter.
5 I get a bit tired of reality TV shows.
6 I don't generally watch much TV.

5
1 documentary 2 everywhere 3 specifically 4 interest
5 separate 6 restaurant 7 listener 8 general

6
Students' own answers.

4e (page 34)

1
a I, we and you; it b active; passive c contracted; uncontracted d formal e Avoid f furthermore
g Share

2
Possible answers:
[1] I've got to admit that [2] I'm [3] not a big fan of stand-up comedy. [4] I always think that it's a rather unnatural thing. The comedian [5] stands up in front of an audience who stare at him or her as if to say, 'Come on, then, make me laugh.' The comedian then has a few minutes to make them laugh or the audience will start to get restless. It's all a bit too aggressive and combative for me. [6] So when [7] I went with an old school friend to see new British comedian Spencer Brown last Tuesday night at the Bristol Comedy Club, [8] I wasn't really looking forward to it.

1 contraction
2 contraction
3 personal details
4 share your feelings
5 active verb
6 conversational linking phrase
7 active verb
8 share your feelings

3
Possible answers:
1 But 2 weren't 3 the rest of the audience seemed to like his act 4 start 5 you think at first 6 then *or* after that 7 that's 8 putting together 9 in fact *or* actually

4
Model answer:
The secret of the show's success is that Spencer Brown really understands his audience and what people find funny. Not only that, but he comes across as a nice guy too. If you are in Bristol, I'd definitely recommend going to see him. He'll be at the Bristol Comedy Club until Saturday 10th December. You'll be smiling for weeks afterwards!

Wordbuilding / Learning skills / Check! (page 35)

1
1 snow**scape** 2 metalwork**er** 3 craftsman**ship**
4 polite**ness** 5 saxophon**ist** 6 romantic**ism**

2
1 surrealism 2 guitarist 3 TV presenter 4 cityscape
5 calmness 6 modernism 7 moonscape 8 musicianship
9 trombonist 10 carpenter 11 directness 12 companionship

4
1 no, not really
2 /ˈkʌmftəbl/
3 You use *either* + singular noun, but *both* + plural noun.
4 Yes, 'it gets on my nerves'.
5 American
6 Yes, it's quite direct.

5
1a Melbourne b All c American
2a few b folk c fan
3a an impersonal tone b a lot of luck c cool down
4a gig; lyrics b sketch; sculpture c play; musical

Unit 5

5a (pages 36 and 37)

1
1 F 2 T 3 T 4 F

2
1 normal 2 floods; winds 3 love 4 co-ordinated
5 depressed 6 safe 7 imaginative *or* innovative
8 practical

3
1 to be 2 seeing 3 to hold 4 to return 5 to resettle
6 building 7 seeing 8 wondering

4
verb + *to* + infinitive: help, hope, want
verb + *someone* + to + infinitive: allow, ask, get, help, want
verb + *-ing*: carry on, enjoy, imagine
verb + *someone* + infinitive: help, imagine, make

5a
verb + *to* + infinitive: choose, learn
verb + *someone* + *to* + infinitive: force, teach
verb + *-ing*: avoid, finish, involve, (not) mind
verb + *someone* + infinitive: let

5b
1 to visit 2 rebuild 3 to participate 4 getting
5 to work 6 learning 7 to do 8 meeting

6
1 pedestrianised 2 mall 3 waterfront 4 luxury
5 housing 6 spaces 7 district 8 centre

7
1 modernise 2 transform 3 spoils 4 demolished
5 redeveloped 6 convert

8a
The fact that most people have returned says a lot about how special this city is. The people who live here can't imagine living anywhere else.
I'm a musician and making a living in New Orleans has always been a challenge. We hoped to see more investment in jobs and tourism after the hurricane.
But since Hurricane Katrina, life has definitely become harder. I love this city, but these days, I'm forced to go out of town to find work.

Answer: Yes, the resident is happy living in New Orleans.

8b
1 can't imagine living 2 hoped to see 3 I'm forced to go

5b (pages 38 and 39)

1
Sentences a and b are true of Monterey today.

2
1 T 2 N 3 F 4 T 5 T 6 T 7 F 8 T

3
1 in the intervening period 2 join (in) the party
3 just like that 4 old-timers 5 set up 6 sample

4
1 dynamic 2 industrial 3 attractive 4 preserved
5 regulated 6 essential

5
1 NC 2 NC 3 C 4 C 5 NC 6 NC 7 C 8 C

6
1 going 2 putting 3 catching 4 to say 5 fishing
6 to make 7 to go 8 eating

7
1 to visit 2 to see 3 to open 4 to do 5 having

8
China – minor
found – drowned
front – hunt
meant – sent
ocean – motion
placed – taste
rule – tool
way – weigh
whale – they'll
where – share

5c (page 40)

1
1 F 2 F 3 F 4 T 5 T

2
1 221 2 pollution 3 possible; easy
4 construction; business 5 materials 6 walk
7 electric *or* electric-powered 8 imported
9 UV 10 farms

3
1 b 2 c 3 c

4
1 pick on 2 pick up 3 pick (me) up 4 take your pick
5 pick holes in 6 pick your brains

5b
architect architectural electricity energy generate
material minimise political sustainable sustainability

5d (page 41)

1
1 d 2 e 3 f 4 c 5 g 6 a 7 b

2
1 public 2 affordable 3 local 4 green 5 pedestrianised
6 leisure

3
1 d 2 b 3 a 4 c

4
1 I find it incredible that
I know what you mean.
2 Personally,
What's your view?
I agree,
We probably need
3 What do you think we should do?
The way I see it,
it really depends on
Exactly.
Are we all agreed on that?
4 If you ask me,
let's not be

5
Students' own answers.

5e (page 42)

1
1 B 2 D 3 A 4 C

2
c quoting what someone (often famous) has said about this problem

3
Possible answers:
(giving a dramatic example) You used to be able to drive from Washington to Boston, a distance of 450 miles, through rich, green landscape. Now the only green you see is the paint on people's houses!

(giving some statistics) In the United States, the area between Boston and Washington DC, a distance of 450 miles, is now a massive urban region with a population of about 50 million – that's almost 17% of the US population on 2% of the US land area.

4
1 In addition
2 Because of this; As a result
3 on the other hand

5b
1 … three acres of land, the house comes with a swimming pool. *or* … coming with three acres of land, the house has a swimming pool.
2 … rising crime, people have moved out of the centre.
3 … a good bus service, we have excellent roads into the city centre. *or* having a good bus service, we have excellent roads into the city centre.
4 … restrictions on building on green spaces, we are redeveloping city centres.

Wordbuilding / Learning skills / Check! (page 43)

1
1 long-term unemployed 2 politically correct
3 economically disadvantaged 4 upwardly mobile
5 ill prepared 6 ethnically mixed 7 highly cultured
8 cleverly designed

2
1 rebuild 2 redecorate 3 retrain 4 readjust 5 redo
6 reread

4
Possible answers:
- It doesn't say who wrote it, but it doesn't seem to be a travel article. The interest seems to be from a historical and urban development perspective.
- The main argument is that a fantastic city has grown up in a place you would not expect it, because of one person's dream and ambition.
- The writer doesn't say whether he/she likes what has happened to Dubai or not, but he/she seems uncertain that it will be a long-term success.
- I agree with the writer's argument. It seems an unsustainable development.

5
1 c 2 c 3 c 4 b 5 b

Unit 6

6a (pages 44 and 45)

1
b Speaker 4 c Speaker 1 e Speaker 2 f Speaker 3
The two extra items are a and d.

2
a Speaker 4 b Speaker 3 d Speaker 1 f Speaker 2
The two extra activities are c and e.

3
1 a 2 b 3 b 4 b 5 c

4
1 Let's not kid ourselves
2 Don't answer
3 You don't have to do
4 not to do
5 I don't think it's extravagant
6 I hope I didn't overdo it.
7 not to let the children know
8 you really mustn't let

5
1 I don't want a coffee now, thanks.
2 I don't think it's a great idea.
3 Let's not do anything to upset them.
4 I hope I didn't give her the wrong impression.
5 You don't have to give the book back to me immediately.
6 Try not to be late, please.
7 You mustn't take food into the library.
8 Have they decided not to stay?

6
1 off *or* holiday 2 catering 3 scenery 4 view
5 airlines 6 luggage *or* baggage 7 journey *or* drive *or* way
8 countryside 9 took 10 suitcase *or* bag

7
1 stay 2 drop 3 eating 4 stay 5 fill 6 join

8
1 In tough economic times, people will try not to spend so much on luxuries and that includes holidays.
2 However, they don't want to go without a holiday altogether, because holidays are an important break from the stresses of work and daily life.

3 You don't have to go abroad to go on holiday. You can have a staycation instead. These have increased in popularity in recent years.
4 I don't think it's a bad trend because it means that people discover more about their own country, and at the same time, they boost the local economy.

6b (pages 46 and 47)

1
1 consultancy-type roles 2 highly skilled professionals
3 four to six months 4 there isn't any flexibility 5 no costs

2
1 c 2 b 3 a 4 c 5 c 6 b

3
1 rewarding 2 tough 3 concentrated 4 fresh 5 set
6 one-off

4
1 Haven't you ever wondered
2 don't you translate
3 Wouldn't you like
4 Won't it harm
5 Aren't you going to lose out
6 Isn't it

5
1 do you 2 wouldn't it 3 is it 4 didn't you
5 mightn't there 6 wouldn't I

6
1 F 2 F 3 R 4 R 5 R 6 F 7 R 8 F

6c (page 48)

1
Items on *NG Endeavour*: a crane, a kayak, a microscope, an inflatable rubber boat, guides

2
1 educational 2 expensive 3 comfortable
4 well-equipped 5 exciting

3
1 fishing 2 $500 3 $1,000 4 video microscope
5 hydrophones 6 photographers 7 naturalists/guides
8 Mediterranean 9 Antarctica 11 dining

4
1 swanning around 2 set in stone 3 a healthy dose of
4 well-off 5 approachable 6 throughout

5
1 **If you had a cruise in mind**, try one of Lindblad's expeditions.
2 **If you don't mind a bit of danger and excitement**, Lindblad cruises are perfect.
3 The cruises are amazing. **Mind you**, they're not cheap.
4 **Bear in mind that** these are not typical cruises.
5 I used to think that cruises were for the old and retired, but **I've changed my mind** (now).
6 **I'm in two minds about** going on one of their cruises.

6b
1 Don't 2 No 3 It doesn't 4 No 5 Don't 6 It doesn't

6d (page 49)

1
1 in 2 up 3 to 4 on 5 out 6 on 7 up 8 out

2
1 He's working. *or* He's at work.
2 He'll get a bus, then walk.
3 At Steve's office.

3
1 The easiest thing is to take the bus.
2 Alternatively, I can take a taxi.
3 I can make my own way.
4 It's only a fifteen-minute bus ride.
5 I'm coming in by train.
6 If I get held up, I'll let you know.

4
1 drive 2 flight 3 ride 4 walk 5 ride 6 crossing

5a
1 d 2b 3a 4e 5c

6
Students' own answers.

6e (page 50)

1
1 She had to pay £30 to carry her coat onto the plane.
2 She wants a refund and she wants the airline to investigate the matter.

2
1 Oxford 2 customer – company 3 formal

3
1 register a complaint 2 unjust 3 stated 4 informed
5 placed 6 attempted 7 wished 8 opted
9 the circumstances 10 investigate

3b
Model answer:

Dear Sir/Madam

I am writing to **register a complaint** about the meal we **were served** on our flight home last week – flight UZ332. On the booking confirmation, it **stated** that we **would be given** breakfast and lunch. **However**, breakfast **only consisted of** a cup of tea and lunch a tuna sandwich. By itself, this would not have been a problem, but **I regret to say that** my husband and I both **suffered** food poisoning from the sandwich.

4
Model answer:

Given the circumstances, I would ask you to do two things. Firstly, please ensure that in future communication with passengers you make it clear what kind of meal will be served. Secondly, please ensure that the food which you provide is fresh and has not been stored in the wrong conditions.

Yours faithfully

Thomas Garcia

Wordbuilding / Learning skills / Check! (page 51)

1
1 in 2 out 3 out 4 in 5 out 6 in 7 in 8 out
9 out *or* in 10 in

2
a fall out (with) b take in c drop in (on) d look in (on)
e fall in (with) f look out g give in (to) h take out
i drop out (of) j give up

3
1 action wanted 2 link the ideas 3 examples 4 spelling

4
1 To complain about an extra charge; this point is made in the opening paragraph
2 Reason for writing; details or facts about the incident; action wanted

3 At the time; by this time; consequently; otherwise; Given these circumstances
4 formal
5 She didn't want to delay other passengers; it's not unreasonable to wear a coat onto a plane

5
1 She took a Japanese holiday in her own city.
2 The Great Continental Divide cycling and hiking trail.
3 In a prison hotel.
4 In an art hotel, e.g. Propeller Island City Lodge, in Berlin.
5 couch surfing

Unit 7

7a (pages 52 and 53)

1
Items which are mentioned: repairing broken water pipes, reusing rainwater, turning salt water into fresh water, making artificial rainclouds

2
1 c 2 b 3 b 4 b 5 c

3
a end-user b hosepipe c water meter d water butt
e on the face of it f ecological footprint g sceptic
h every cloud has a silver lining

4
1 hadn't imposed; would be (mixed conditional)
2 had; would use (second conditional)
3 introduce; will buy (first conditional) *or* introduced; would buy (second conditional)
4 was; wouldn't need (second conditional)
5 weren't; would have been built (mixed conditional)
6 hadn't been; would feel (mixed conditional)
7 works; are (zero conditional)
8 had thought; would be (mixed conditional)

6
1 run out of 2 save 3 waste; conserve 4 preserve
5 protect 6 spend; consume

7b (pages 54 and 55)

1
1 oil tanker 2 oil rig 3 oil slick 4 oil refinery
5 oil field 6 oil well 7 oil barrel 8 oil pipeline

2
No, he doesn't.

3
1 c 2 a 3 b 4 a 5 c 6 b

4
1 would go 2 was able 3 hadn't started 4 have
5 was 6 ran

5
1 drove 2 had 3 would stop 4 had bought
5 not think 6 would become 7 had seen 8 didn't speak

7
The recent discovery of oil in the tar sands of Alberta has put Canada in third place in the world in oil reserves.

However, extracting this oil creates two to four times the quantity of greenhouse gases as conventional methods of extraction.

As a result, Canada has been under a lot of pressure to limit the environmental impact of its new oil industry.

7c (page 56)

1
1 forest, Cancún, no 2 giraffe, yes 3 tree, Britain, yes

2
1 F 2 T 3 T 4 N 5 N 6 F

3
1 rotting 2 classic 3 sale 4 victims 5 heroic
6 wonderful 7 small 8 rarest

4
1 classic 2 a decade 3 a victim 4 buried
5 for sale 6 rotting

5
Emotive words: back-breaking, deplore, desperate, majestic, obsessed with

6
1 rescue 2 deprived 3 giant 4 exploit 5 wonderful
6 most threatened 7 plummeting 8 overdeveloped

7d (page 57)

1
1 F 2 A 3 F 4 A

2
1 understand each other better
2 in rich countries to have cheaper goods and also goods out of season
3 natural economic phenomenon
4 the gap between the world's rich and poor

3
1 not, point 2 just, accept 3 be honest 4 approaching, wrong 5 Imagine 6 let, give 7 doubt

4
Speaker 1: c and e
Speaker 2: d
Speaker 3: a and d
Speaker 4: d

5a
1 Globalisation may have helped the rich, but it hasn't helped the poor.
2 Globalisation is not something that has been invented; it's a natural phenomenon.
3 I like having things that I can't buy locally, but I don't actually need them.
4 Globalisation doesn't harm poor countries; it helps them.
5 I wish you were right, but the facts show the opposite.

6
Students' own answers.

7e (page 58)

1
1 The writer feels that people waste resources such as food, energy and clothes.
2 There will be no more resources left.

2a
1 who live in more difficult circumstances than us
2 which is near its sell-by date
3 such as flat-screen TVs, computers or mobile phones
4 with only one driver in them
5 especially items of fashion clothing

2b
Possible answers:
1 with over 70 apartments
2 such as the black poplar tree, which is not found anywhere else in the city

3 where old and young people can come and relax
4 like the old industrial estate in Meadow Leys
5 because they are ugly and in need of modernising

3
1 c 2 b 3 e 4 a 5 d

4
1 to wait 2 calling 3 do 4 to know

Wordbuilding / Learning skills / Check! (page 59)

1
1 wind instrument 2 air bridge 3 wind farm
4 wind chill 5 water leak 6 air force 7 water jug
8 air vent 9 water lily

2
sunrise and sunset

4
1 Globalisation helps people in rich countries.
2 They can have goods out of season.
3 But to be honest, I don't need flowers imported from Africa in December.

6
Across: 1 renewable 4 unique 5 ecosystem 7 salt 10 Colorado 12 save 13 well
Down: 1 reuse 2 loggers 3 extract 6 scarce 8 Aral 9 wool 11 oil

Unit 8

8a (pages 60 and 61)

1
Across: 1 hard 3 soft 7 editorial 8 news
Down: 2 article 4 feature 5 headline 6 column

2
1 cover; 1982
2 Nancy; Week

3
1 F 2 T 3 F 4 T 5 F 6 F 7 T 8 F

5
1 of manipulating reality.
2 altering the image *or* that they had altered the image.
3 doing anything wrong. *or* that they had done anything wrong.
4 modern technology for making it easy to alter images.
5 their designers (that it is OK) to alter images for covers.
6 about being given a false impression. *or* that they had been given a false impression.
7 not to trust a photo if there's anything important riding on it.

6
1 for invading 2 (for) taking 3 for manipulating
4 to alter 5 touching 6 to add 7 for making 8 to accept

7
1 capture the moment
2 open the shutter
3 record events
4 see through the lens
5 take a photo
6 take a snapshot

8
1 recommends using an analogue camera
2 encourages you to look at the preview before you take a photo; keeps you in the moment
3 that with a digital camera, you need more time to edit the images after they've been taken
4 you can make them look like the image as you saw it

8b (pages 62 and 63)

1
1 b 2 d 3 a 4 c

2
a 3 b 2 c 3 d 4 e 1 f 1

3
1 wrecked 2 donations 3 longevity 4 zimmer frame
5 brainchild 6 brighten up 7 plunged 8 speeding

4
1 it is estimated that rioters
2 It was reported that
3 It is believed that
4 It is not thought that

5
1 It is said that
2 It is understood that
3 It was known that
4 It was believed that
5 It has been estimated that
6 It is thought that
7 It had been hoped that
8 It is supposed that

6
1 It is said that for every negative, there is always a positive.
2 It is expected that Mr Biber will carry on doing what he loves.
3 In the past, it was thought that a glass of red wine a day helped/would help you to live longer.
4 It is not recommended that you eat fast food if you want to live longer.
5 It was hoped that secret gifts would brighten up someone's day.
6 It was supposed that the tree prevented/had prevented the car falling further.
7 It was considered that the man had been/was lucky to survive the accident.
8 It has been reported that the idea was very successful.

7
amusing – serious
charming – dreary
inspiring – uninspiring
quirky – ordinary
encouraging – depressing
optimistic – pessimistic

8c (page 64)

1
1 T 2 F 3 F

2
1 view 2 wonders 3 beauty 4 pipeline 5 Strictly
6 jumped 7 dilemma 8 the last word

3
1 strictly speaking 2 wonders 3 have the last word
4 balanced view 5 dilemma 6 jump the gun

4
1 b 2 b 3 a 4 a

5
1 word of mouth 2 eat my words
3 one person's word against another's
4 don't take my word for it 5 gave his word
6 From the word go 7 was lost for words
8 have the last word

8d (page 65)

1
1 take (B) 2 gets (B) 3 spread (D) 4 Take (D)
5 blown (D) 6 take (D)

2
1 Philip has been signed up by a theatrical agent.
2 Kate
3 Not to tell anyone. Patrick wants to keep quiet about it.

3
1 about; Guess 2 apparently 3 reckons 4 pinch
5 according to 6 heard 7 gossip 8 seems; supposedly

4
1 comedy 2 festival 3 apparently 4 reckon 5 according
6 difficult 7 agency 8 theatrical

5
Students' own answers.

8e (page 66)

1
1 attend, hold
2 make, put forward
3 make, reach
4 discuss, weigh up
5 draft, write

2
1 A meeting was held to discuss how to raise the money.
2 All the options were discussed.
3 One suggestion was to ask the local council for help.
4 Another idea was to have some fun events.
5 It was agreed that organising events would take too long.
6 No decision was reached/could be reached about funding the project.

3
1 Advantages: the incinerator will generate electricity and dispose of waste
Disadvantages: it will cause a lot of pollution
2 Everyone in the area would sign a petition. Harry would research another kind of plant.
3 To present some alternative locations.

4
1 a meeting was held to decide
2 It was suggested
3 It was agreed
4 It was thought that
5 The point was made
6 It was proposed that
7 This option would be researched and discussed

Wordbuilding / Learning skills / Check! (page 67)

1
1 worrying 2 confusing 3 refreshing 4 charming
5 inspiring 6 depressing 7 touching 8 tiring

2
1 inventive 2 persuasive 3 creative 4 competitive
5 productive 6 talkative 7 protective 8 unresponsive

3, 4 and 5
Students' own answers.

6
1a words b sell c fast
2a zero b iconic c exinct
3a mouth b feel-good c spread d feature

Unit 9

9a (pages 68 and 69)

1
1 small village in Illinois
2 radio broadcaster; (an) actor
3 the Soviet Union
4 was not very clever *or* read the lines given to him
5 listen to people *or* make people feel special
6 economic growth

2
1 b 2 a 3 a 4 b 5 b 6 a

3
1 graduated 2 worked 3 follow *or* pursue 4 joining
5 did 6 become

4
1 the United Arab Emirates, the Netherlands
2 the Amazon River, the countryside, the Moon
3 the weekend, the spring
4 the police, the poor
All the other nouns take zero article.

5
1 the; the; – 2 the; – 3 the; the 4 the; – 5 the 6 the
7 –; – 8 –; – 9 the 10 the

6
1 /r/ 2 /j/ 3 /j/ 4 /j/ 5 /r/ 6 /r/ 7 /j/
8 /w/ 9 /w/

7
1 I guess I was lucky to do a subject that not many other people at college did. I studied plant sciences and after my course, I got a job as a research assistant at the Institute of Botany.
2 It's not easy to be an artist and make a living from it. You are always wondering if it would be better just to get a job with a regular income.
3 I was always told that having good qualifications and the right degree opens doors, but actually it's good communication skills that help you advance in an organisation.

8
1 background 2 experience 3 qualifications
4 qualities 5 knowledge 6 talents

9b (pages 70 and 71)

1
1 My mission is to find simple, inexpensive ways to monitor health
2 these medicines can cause liver damage
3 The small piece of paper is a low-tech tool
4 to attend university
5 I want all women to believe in themselves and know they can transform society *or* to encourage young women who attend university abroad to bring their skills back to their homelands

2
1 c 2 b 3 c 4 a 5 b 6 b

3
1 a 2 b 3 c 4 b 5 c 6 c

4
1 … which detects disease by analysing bodily fluids.
2 … who attend university abroad
3 … which show up in less than a minute
4 … costing just a penny
5 … pioneered by a team at Harvard University

5
1 The piece of paper, **which** is the size of a postage stamp, could save thousands of lives. *or* The piece of paper, **which** could save thousands of lives, is the size of a postage stamp.
2 The charity 'Diagnostics for All', **which** was co-founded by Sindi, produces the tool. *or* The charity 'Diagnostics for All', **which** produces the tool, was co-founded by Sindi.
3 The tool will be used in developing countries **where** it is difficult to find clinics.
4 People take powerful drugs, **which** can cause liver damage, to combat diseases.
5 The results show up on the paper, **whose** colour changes if there is a problem.
6 Sindi went to England **when** she was a young woman.
7 Sindi, **who** was the first Saudi woman to study biotechnology at Cambridge, later went to Harvard. *or* Sindi, **who** later went to Harvard, was the first Saudi woman to study biotechnology at Cambridge.
8 Sindi has become a role model for other women **who** want to follow her example.

6
1 Sindi's low-tech tool helps people **suffering from the negative effects of the drugs**.
2 People **living far away from hospitals and clinics** will benefit from this technology.
3 The same medicines, **designed to fight disease**, can also harm people.
4 Sindi, **determined to succeed**, studied up to twenty hours a day.
5 Sindi uses her own experience to inspire other women **wishing to become scientists**.
6 A new foundation, **launched** recently by Sindi, offers help to young women **wanting to follow a career in science**.

7
1 determination 2 accomplishment 3 inspiration 4 passion

8
1 passionate 2 articulate 3 analytical 4 patient
5 independent 6 adaptable 7 daring 8 easy-going

9c (page 72)

1
1 W 2 W 3 W 4 W 5 W 6 M 7 M and W 8 W

2
1 T 2 T 3 F 4 F 5 T 6 T

3
1 adventur**ous** 2 effect**ive** 3 sensit**ive** 4 car**ing**
5 assert**ive** 6 persuas**ive** 7 autocrat**ic** 8 inclus**ive**

4a
1 effective 2 sensitive 3 assertive 4 persuasive
5 inclusive
The stress always falls on the second syllable. The exception is 'sensitive', where it falls on the first syllable.

4b
1 protective 2 creative 3 perceptive 4 imaginative
5 responsive 6 impulsive

5
1 j 2 a 3 c 4 h 5 b 6 e 7 f 8 g 9 d 10 i

9d (page 73)

1
1 in 2 with 3 at 4 of 5 to 6 with 7 on 8 about

2
A job to lead outdoor activities and expeditions for young people.

3
1
Applicant 1: good at working with young children
Applicant 2: canoeing, water sports and outdoor activities; good organisational skills
Applicant 3: good at a number of different sports; experienced PE teacher

2
Applicant 1: hasn't got experience working with this age group
Applicant 2: hasn't got experience of mountaineering
Applicant 3: hasn't got experience of leading expeditions

4
1 participating 2 to leave 3 travelling 4 doing
5 to work *or* on working 6 to find out *or* in finding out

6
Students' own answers.

9e (page74)

1
1 b 2 d 3 a 4 f 5 c 6 e

2
1 marketing jobs
2 Japanese and English
3 she's highly qualified

3a
1 My job involves advising a British supermarket on their market plan for Japan.
2 I was responsible for the 'Winnie the Pooh' account.
3 I translated marketing documents for various British and US companies.
4 I'm currently doing a distance learning MBA.

3b
1 Specialist website designer
2 Designing interactive website for local sports and leisure centre
3 Computer programmer, British Telecom
Designer, patient communications website, local hospital
Set up company in 2010
4 Buckingham Grammar School;
Liverpool University

Wordbuilding / Learning skills / Check! (page 75)

1
The verbs which do not collocate are:
1 do 2 make 3 get 4 make 5 acquire 6 win 7 own
8 work 9 earn 10 take on

2
1 took 2 follow 3 get *or* do 4 had 5 get
6 joined *or* set up 7 got *or* gained 8 acquire *or* learn

3
1 d 2 f 3 b 4 h 5 e 6 a 7 c 8 g

4
1 felt 2 definite article 3 acquire *or* get 4 yes
5 semi-formal

5
1 a a mahout b an explorer
2 step, leap, mankind
3 a the Atlantic Ocean d the USA e the Moon
4 c

Unit 10

10a (pages 76 and 77)

1
Speaker 1: e
Speaker 2: d
Speaker 3: a
Speaker 4: c

2
a 2 b 4 c 2 d 1 e 3 f 4

3
1 b 2 a 3 a 4 c 5 b 6 a

4
Possible answers:
1 take 2 think 3 teach 4 will follow *or* follow 5 will design *or* design 6 are always fighting 7 squabbling 8 argue *or* will argue 9 say 10 helps *or* will help 11 tend 12 generally follow *or* will generally follow 13 will be 14 always follow *or* will always follow 15 often get *or* will often get

5
1 She's always talking
2 He's always asking if
3 She's always spending ages
4 He's always talking
5 He's always playing
6 She's always leaving

6
1 brought 2 spoil 3 punished 4 discipline 5 disobey 6 nagging 7 rebelled 8 pestering 9 give 10 reward

7
Everything depends on what you see as the future role of your children. In other words, what is it that you are raising them to do?
Do you want them to be good members of society? If so, you will teach them values such as obeying the law, co-operating with others and generally being good citizens.
Or do you want them to be successful individuals? If so, you will help them to be free thinkers and to be independent.
Or is it important that they are good family members? Then you will teach them to respect their elders and to follow family traditions.

10b (pages 78 and 79)

1
c

2
1 b 2 c 3 a 4 a 5 c

3
1 used to eat 2 used to use 3 are used to eating 4 have got used to eating *or* usually eat 5 usually eat out 6 are used to seeing 7 used to eat 8 usually eat

4
1 didn't use to cook 2 used to cook 3 wanted 4 used to hang *or* would hang 5 was 6 had 7 used to cook *or* would cook 8 were used to doing *or* used to do

5a
/uː/: blue, fortune, lunar, rude, suit, truce
/juː/: consume, humanity, humour, menu, used, usually

6
1 D/S, P 2 F, F, P 3 S/F, P 4 P, D

10c (page 80)

1
1 F 2 F 3 T 4 T 5 F 6 T

2
1 d 2 b

3
1 rather 2 Unlike 3 little 4 such 5 At worst

5
a common good
b common interest

6
Across: 4 ground 5 sense
Down: 1 knowledge 2 mistakes 3 interest 4 good

10d (page 81)

1
1 honeymoon 2 vows 3 stag 4 veil 5 bells 6 groom 7 proposal

2
1 It's a sign of wealth and social status.
2 For the bride not working.
3 the bride's family
4 the groom's family
5 They bring gifts.
6 clothes and jewellery

3
1 symbolises 2 rule 3 customary 4 marks 5 occasion 6 place 7 traditional 8 On

4
1 /z/ 2 /s/ 3 /z/ 4 /s/ 5 /s/ 6 /z/ 7 /s/ 8 /s/ 9 /z/ 10 /s/ 11 /z/ 12 /z/

5
Students' own answers.

10e (page 82)

1
Possible answer:

Hi Annabelle

Very good to see you the other day. Hope you got back to Leipzig safely. I forgot to mention that I'm travelling to Poland next month on business to visit a supplier. I've really got no idea about business customs in Poland and wondered if there was anything I should know especially. For example, should I take some gifts with me? Will they be put out that I don't speak any Polish? I certainly don't want to put my foot in it with my hosts in any way.

I don't want to bother you, but if you've got a moment to write me a few words of advice, I'd be really grateful.

All the best

2
Possible answers:
1 Hi 2 Good to see 3 thanks 4 helping 5 Unfortunately 6 here's 7 don't 8 big 9 be embarrassing 10 You'll 11 seem *or* are 12 That's 13 I'm sure 14 they'll 15 About 16 It's 17 Hope 18 let me know 19 when you get back 20 All the best

Wordbuilding / Learning skills / Check! (page 83)

1
1 bride and groom
2 husband and wife
3 friends and family
4 suit and tie
5 food and drink
6 singing and dancing
7 bits and pieces
8 time and trouble
9 plans and arrangements
10 pomp and ceremony
11 fun and games
12 life and soul

2
1 pomp and ceremony 2 time and trouble 3 bits and pieces 4 life and soul 5 friends and family 6 suit and tie

5
1 in 2 out 3 back 4 in 5 sense 6 ground 7 foot 8 hen

Unit 11

11a (pages 84 and 85)

1
c

2
1 b 2 c 3 c 4 a 5 c 6 a

3
1 document 2 trace; record 3 seeks out 4 express
5 store 6 save

4
1 succeeded in discovering
2 were able to help
3 managed to build
4 was able to help
5 could bring
6 couldn't save

5
Possible answers:
1 managed to find *or* was able to find
2 could speak *or* was able to speak
3 never managed to convince *or* never succeeded in convincing *or* were never able to convince
4 couldn't understand *or* wasn't able to understand
5 could express *or* was able to express
6 could remember *or* was able to remember *or* managed to remember *or* succeeded in remembering

6
1 c 2 f 3 h 4 g 5 d 6 a 7 b 8 e

7
1 pick (it) up
2 inspire *or* motivate *or* engage with
3 ignorant
4 have a basic grasp
5 engage with *or* grasp *or* pick up
6 take in *or* grasp

8a
1a Munichi b Wappo
2a Swarthmore b Pennsylvania
3a Arunchal b Koro
4 chary
5 floccinaucinihilipilification

8b
a 5 b 2a c 4 d 1b e 3b

11b (pages 86 and 87)

1
a 2 b 1 c 3

2
1 T 2 F 3 F 4 N 5 F 6 N 7 F 8 T 9 T

3
1 blank (something) out 2 ran into 3 came up (to)
4 turned out (that) 5 come across 6 get away with

4
Paragraph 1
1 My sister and I **were just about to go** to bed … *or* **were just going to go** to bed …
2 My sister **was going to say** goodnight … *or* **was about to say** goodnight …

Paragraph 2
3 I **would have asked** his name …
4 I **was supposed to know** …

Paragraph 3
5 who **was going to give** evidence in court … *or* **was supposed to give** evidence in court … *or* **was about to give evidence** in court …
6 her neighbour **wouldn't get away with** it … *or* **wasn't going to get away with** it …

5
1 was going to write *or* would have written
2 was just about to book; would be full
3 would speak
4 would have lasted *or* was supposed to last; were about to finish *or* were going to finish
5 was going to take *or* would have taken *or* was supposed to take
6 was just about to ask *or* was just going to ask

6a
1 I was going to email him, but I decided it would better to speak face to face.
2 He was supposed to get here early, but he's already ten minutes late.
3 I would have come by train, but there's a strike on at the moment.
4 She said she would be pleased if I talked to him, but she seemed really angry.
5 I was about to buy a flat, but Katie said I could rent hers for six months while she was away.
6 Liz was going to be in charge of the project, but now she's just acting as an advisor.

6b
1 I was going to email him, but I decided it would better to speak face to face.
2 He was supposed to get here early, but he's already ten minutes late.
3 I would have come by train, but there's a strike on at the moment.
4 She said she would be pleased if I talked to him, but she seemed really angry.
5 I was about to buy a flat, but Katie said I could rent hers for six months while she was away.
6 Liz was going to be in charge of the project, but now she's just acting as an advisor.

7
1 c 2 d 3 a 4 e 5 b

11c (page 88)

1
1 border collie 2 crow 3 dolphin 4 Bonobo monkey
5 scrub-jay

2
a 3 b 4 c 1 d 5 e 2

3
a 2 b 3 c 5 d 1 e 4

4
1 smart 2 inventive 3 playful 4 expressive
5 mischevious

5
1 walk 2 late 3 mistakes 4 tricks 5 lesson 6 live
7 way 8 heart

11d (page 89)

1
1 mean 2 speak 3 explain 4 'm 5 saying 6 give
7 take 8 catch *or* hear

2
1 Greek and Roman history
2 He doesn't have as much background knowledge as the other students.
3 Reading some history *or* a book by Herodotus.

3
1 what the course is going to be about
2 no previous knowledge of ancient history is needed
3 stories like the war at Troy and so on
4 a book I could read now, outside class
5 Herodotus

4
1 me 5 me 6 me
The other sentences don't need an indirect personal object.

6
Students' own answers.

11e (page 90)

1
1 c 2 e 3 d 4 b 5 a
The writer's application for a course has been rejected even though he/she applied before the deadline.

2
1 While we sympathise with your situation, it is too late to do anything about it now.
2 Although you sent your form in before the deadline, we had already received too many applications.
3 You say in your letter that we have no right to do this, but in actual fact, the college has the right to close the application process early.
4 We don't 'make up the rules as we go along' as you suggest. On the contrary, we are very careful to follow the rules.
5 Whereas most colleges would keep your application fee, we are refunding it to you.

3
Model answer:

Dear Sir/Madam

I am writing to inform you that I will be unable to attend the accountancy course (B102) this term owing to a misunderstanding.

When I enrolled for the course, I had assumed it was an evening class. In actual fact it turns out to be on Tuesdays between 10 a.m. and 12.30 p.m. I have asked my employer if it would be possible to release me for this period each Tuesday. Although they would like to do this, they say that the timing makes it impossible.

While I realise that this is probably my fault for not reading the timetable carefully enough, I hope you will be sympathetic. I hope to enrol on a future course, but for the moment I would be grateful if you could refund the course fees I have paid.

I look forward to hearing from you.

Yours faithfully

Mark Riley

Wordbuilding / Learning skills / Check! (page 91)

1
1 e *or* d 2 a 3 d *or* e 4 c 5 b 6 f

2, 3, 4 and 5
Students' own answers.

6
Across: 1 engage 5 selective 7 tip 8 external 10 catch
Down: 2 grasp 3 succeed 4 botanist 6 ignorant
8 error 9 late

Unit 12

12a (pages 92 and 93)

1
1 savers and spenders
2 No, these stereotypes are too simplistic.

2
1 b 2 a 3 c 4 a 5 b 6 c

3
fund – finance
prudent – careful
transaction – deal
wages – salaries
wasteful – extravagant

4
1 hard up 2 afford 3 reasonable; cheap 4 pricey
5 earnings 6 well off 7 loaded

R	H	P	I	M	O	I	N
E	A	R	N	I	N	G	S
A	R	I	C	C	F	O	T
S	D	C	H	E	A	P	O
O	U	E	S	O	F	U	L
N	P	Y	B	A	F	L	E
A	W	E	L	L	O	F	F
B	I	L	E	F	R	A	T
L	O	A	D	E	D	E	S
E	S	T	O	N	R	I	A

5
1 just *or* also
2 as well *or* too; only
3 even *or* also
4 also
5 only

6
1 Some people believe that if you go through life ONLY saving money, you will never have any fun. *or* Some people believe that if you ONLY go through life saving money, you will never have any fun.
2 Some people carry on spending money EVEN when they can't afford to.
3 You can guard against bad times by putting aside JUST a small amount of money each week.
4 If ONLY a few people save money, the banks won't have any to lend.
5 I'm not the only person who has debts. Other people ALSO have them. *or* Other people have them ALSO.
6 Attitude to money is partly a cultural thing, but it has something to do with your upbringing AS WELL.
7 Some people are careful with money in hard times and in good times TOO.
8 Borrowers admit that EVEN they sometimes borrow money irresponsibly. *or* EVEN borrowers admit that they sometimes borrow money irresponsibly..

7
1 payments 2 spending 3 investment 4 loan 5 grant
6 borrowing 7 debts 8 earnings

8
I think that people often get into debt because they want a lifestyle that they can't really afford.

It's a lifestyle which is sold to them constantly through advertisements, for example on TV and in magazines.

This desire to have a better lifestyle can affect some governments too. They want to improve their citizens' standard of living so that people will vote for them again.

12b (pages 94 and 95)

1
a

2
1 F 2 T 3 T 4 T 5 N 6 T 7 N 8 T

3
1 track 2 striking 3 sufficient 4 competent
5 of choice 6 infirm 7 blacksmith 8 trade

4
1 have people work
2 get their work done
3 get your labourers to work
4 had 10,000 slaves a year sent
5 got the slaves to work
6 had their slaves work
7 got them to learn
8 had cheap cotton shipped

5a
/ʃ/: abolished, sugar
/ʧ/: cheap, riches
/ʒ/: decision, usually
/ʤ/: carriage, wages

6
1 fit 2 put 3 decorate 4 assemble 5 fixed 6 tiled
7 plaster 8 hang

7
1 b 2 f 3 a 4 d 5 c 6 e

12c (page 96)

1
b

2
1 c 2 b 3 b 4 c 5 a

3
1 hard up 2 hard-headed 3 hard bargain
4 hard feelings 5 hard done by

4
1a is running hard
1b is hardly running
2a hardly works *or* is hardly working
2b works hard *or* is working hard
3a hardly know
4a thought hard
4b hardly thought
5a hardly tried
5b tried hard

12d (page 97)

1
1 d 2 b 3 f 4 a 5 c 6 e

2
1 a leaving party for a colleague
2 a reduction in the price

3
1 honest 2 mind 3 hoping 4 would 5 face 6 shoes
7 appreciate 8 key

4
1 Can I just explain our position?
2 To tell you the truth, …
3 If you look at it from our side, …
4 That's going to be a bit of a sticking point.
5 To be perfectly honest, …
6 What you have to bear in mind is …

5
1 I'm afraid that would be difficult for me.
2 Would you move a bit on the price?
3 Would you be willing to negotiate?
4 I would need to have some kind of guarantee.
5 When would you need to know?
6 I wouldn't want to put you to any trouble.

6
Students' own answers.

12e (page 98)

1
The report is about the catering for the Annual General Meeting.

2
1
- How much food do we need to provide?
- Cost?
- Any special dietary needs?

2
- Hot food: about £10 per person
- Cold food: about £7 per person

3
I propose that we go with Angel Foods. They seemed to understand better what we want, and I think they will do it all for a better price.

3
Summary
I visited our caterer to discuss the arrangements for our office party on 12th December.

Food
- Sandwiches: £6 per person
- Sandwiches and cold canapés: £8 per person
- Sandwiches and hot canapés: £10 per person

Drinks
- The caterer can provide drinks or we can buy our own.
- Charge: £1 per person.

Recommendation
I propose we go for the mixture of sandwiches and cold canapés, and provide our own drinks.

Wordbuilding / Learning skills / Check! (page 99)

1
1 the rich 2 the unemployed 3 the poor 4 the homeless
5 the elderly 6 the famous 7 the blind 8 the deaf
9 the illiterate 10 the sick

2
1 P 2 N 3 N 4 N 5 X 6 P 7 X 8 X 9 N 10 N

3 and 4
Students' own answers.

5
1 relative 2 investing 3 cleaner 4 hunter 5 end
6 spending
Word: RICHES

IELTs practice test

Listening

1 C so my flatmate was saying
2 B Just the morning or the afternoon would suit me fine
3 A you'd have to sign up like anyone else – and there's a monthly fee
4 A tips on how to put a CV together
5 D a seminar led by one of the big recruitment agencies
6 JAYNES J.A.Y.N.E.S
7 Business Studies M: Which faculty's that? Economics? F: Business Studies actually
8 technical translations This time she's doing technical translations
9 construction industry He's going to be talking about openings in the construction industry
10 Geology He's working in the Geology department
11 C visitors can walk along a pathway not far from the base
12 B an adult single ticket would cost £6.50 in the summer months and £5.50 at other times of year, whereas a family ticket would cost either £24.00 or £20.00.
13 C/D explore the universe using hands-on activities
14 D/C the glass-walled café with outside terrace
15 Botany it wasn't the Astrophysics department that bought it though, but the Botany department.
16 meteor shower installed just in time to observe a meteor shower
17 1947 in 1947 the 218-foot Transit Telescope
18 Mark 1/One/I This was named the Mark One Telescope
19 solar system a scale model of the solar system
20 World Heritage to place Jodrell Bank on the UK shortlist for consideration as a site with World Heritage status
21 A how you balance these two aspects is up to you
22 C I hadn't even chosen a speciality – that made it tough.
23 B I'd have done better with a straight four-week split.
24 A talk to people ...that's how I found the one I went with
25 emergency I went for emergency
26 beach photos ... of the beach that drew me to Belize
27 300,000 with 300,000 people
28 (the) North up north where I was
29 Cuban a lot of the doctors working there were actually Cuban
30 teaching (the staff) I'd rather think of teaching the staff
31 One/1 metre/meter that grows to around one metre
32 Dark brown the male ... is a dark brown
33 Silver(-)grey/grey the female is distinguishable by its silver-grey skin
34 (dense) undergrowth has a preference for dense undergrowth
35 Lizard(s) tends to rely on lizards as its main source of food
36 Bird Bird island, the place where one was eventually spotted
37 (six-week) survey They commissioned a six-week survey
38 100 supporting a racer population of around 100 individuals
39 B/C The right kind of habitat is not found over a wide area
40 C/B although the snake's habitat does remain vulnerable to hurricane damage

Reading

1 TRUE Start by identifying the appropriate granting body to contact
2 TRUE check ... the deadline for the submission of proposals
3 FALSE Your proposal should be written out in the format stipulated
4 FALSE It's a good idea to propose only those objectives that you feel confident of achieving within the grant period
5 NOT GIVEN (there is no mention of whether this is advisable or not)
6 TRUE cover what is already known about the problem in scientific literature
7 FALSE In addition, many forms now have a section ... required to describe how the research is likely to contribute to economic development
8 NOT GIVEN (there is no mention of whether they do this or not)
9 TRUE state clearly that you're aware of the limitations of your approach
10 FALSE describe briefly any particular strengths of your laboratory
11 iii like to see a concise description of the results of any work you have already carried out
12 v your application should include latitude, longitude, elevation, vegetation ...
13 vii Describe how you plan to identify people to take part in experiments
14 ii lab procedures .... a brief description of the various analytical techniques that you will carry out
15 vi how it will be entered on a computerised database and what software will be used
16 viii the partners with whom you intend to work
17 C evidence for at least 15 separate occasions when it acted as a home
18 B predate other known examples of plant matting by approximately 50,000 years
19 A a tree whose foliage contains chemicals that kill biting insects. Dr Wadley thus thinks ... mattresses on which the inhabitants slept.
20 A a range of hitherto unknown artefacts ... pictograms
21 C a range of hitherto unknown artefacts ... arrows
22 D a range of hitherto unknown artefacts ... needles
23 (a/the) tree(s) They probably settled in trees at night
24 climbing they still retained features useful for climbing, such as curved fingers and long arms
25 chimpanzees just as chimpanzees do today
26 fire once hominids learned how to control fire they discovered they could sleep on the ground
27 grass Neanderthals were also building grass beds
28 cellulose *Macrotermes* species live on cellulose
29 gardens by cultivating gardens for fungi
30 (digestible) nutrients which can turn it into digestible nutrients
31 heat heat from the fungi's metabolism and termites' bodies
32 (central) chimney causes stagnant air ... to rise up a central chimney
33 base air is sucked in at the base

34 humidity their temperature and humidity closely controlled

35 TRUE This simple ... idea spawned at least one artificial imitation

36 TRUE rules out any kind of buoyant flow ... showed little evidence of steady, convective air circulation

37 NOT GIVEN (there is no mention of their methodology)

38 TRUE the mound functions as a giant lung

39 FALSE Turner thinks there's something to be gleaned from the termites' approach.

40 FALSE idea among the biologists that architects could learn much from us. I think the opposite is also true